Praise for *Six Impossible Things*

'[A]n accessible primer on all things quantum … rigorous and chatty.'
Sunday Times

'Gribbin has inspired generations with his popular science writing, and this, his latest offering, is a compact and delightful summary of the main contenders for a true interpretation of quantum mechanics. … If you've never puzzled over what our most successful scientific theory means, or even if you have and want to know what the latest thinking is, this new book will bring you up to speed faster than a collapsing wave function.'
Jim Al-Khalili

'Gribbin gives us a feast of precision and clarity, with a phenomenal amount of information for such a compact space. It's a TARDIS of popular science books, and I loved it. … This could well be the best piece of writing this grand master of British popular science has ever produced, condensing as it does many years of pondering the nature of quantum physics into a compact form.'
Brian Clegg, popularscience.co.uk

'Elegant and accessible … Highly recommended for students of the sciences and fans of science fiction, as well as for anyone who is curious to understand the strange world of quantum physics.'
Forbes

Praise for *Seven Pillars of Science*

'[In] the last couple of years we have seen a string of books that pack bags of science in a digestible form into a small space. John Gribbin has already proved himself a master of this approach with his *Six Impossible Things*, and he's done it again … [*Seven Pillars of Science* is] light, to the point and hugely informative … It packs in the science, tells an intriguing story and is beautifully packaged.'

Brian Clegg, popularscience.co.uk

Praise for *Eight Improbable Possibilities*

'We loved this book … deeply thought-provoking and a book that we want to share with as many people as possible.'

Irish Tech News

'[Gribbin] deftly joins the dots to reveal a bigger picture that is even more awe-inspiring than the sum of its parts.'

Physics World

'A fascinating journey into the world of scientific oddities and improbabilities.'

Lily Pagano, *Reaction*

'Gribbin casts a wide net and displays his breadth of knowledge in packing a lot into each chapter … a brief read, but one that may inspire readers to dig deeper.'

Giles Sparrow, *BBC Sky at Night Magazine*

Praise for *Nine Musings on Time*

'The yarn of time ravels into a rich tapestry of both science and speculation, under John Gribbin's deft hand.'

David Brin, Hugo Award-winning science fiction writer, author of *The Postman*, the book that inspired the Kevin Costner movie

TEN

TANTALISING

TRUTHS

TEN

TANTALISING

TRUTHS

*Why the Sky Is
Blue, and Other
Big Answers to
Simple Questions*

JOHN

GRIBBIN

ICON

22

Published in the UK and USA in 2023 by
Icon Books Ltd, Omnibus Business Centre,
39–41 North Road, London N7 9DP
email: info@iconbooks.com
www.iconbooks.com

ISBN: 978-183773-100-8
ebook: 978-183773-112-1

Text copyright © 2023 John and Mary Gribbin

The authors have asserted their moral rights.

No part of this book may be reproduced in any form, or by any means, without prior permission in writing from the publisher.

Typesetting by SJmagic DESIGN SERVICES, India

Printed and bound in the UK

CONTENTS

John Gribbin's numerous best-selling books include *In Search of Schrödinger's Cat*, *The Universe: A Biography*, *13.8: The Quest to Find the True Age of the Universe and the Theory of Everything*, and *Out of the Shadow of a Giant: How Newton Stood on the Shoulders of Hooke and Halley*.

His most recent book is *Nine Musings on Time: Science Fiction, Science Fact, and the Truth About Time Travel*. His earlier title, *Six Impossible Things: The 'Quanta of Solace' and the Mysteries of the Subatomic World*, was shortlisted for the Royal Society Insight Investment Science Book Prize for 2019. He is an Honorary Senior Research Fellow at the University of Sussex and was described as 'one of the finest and most prolific writers of popular science around' by the *Spectator*.

For William, Beatrice and Florence: my chief inquisitors

tantalising:

possessing a quality that arouses or stimulates desire or interest

Merriam-Webster Dictionary

PREFACE

Tantalising Questions

When I wrote my book *Six Impossible Things*, I did not anticipate it being the beginning of a series. But it seemed to strike a chord with people who wanted simple answers to big questions in science, such as the nature of quantum reality, the emergence of life on Earth and the origin of the Universe. Having done my best to tackle these issues with *Seven Pillars of Science* and *Eight Improbable Possibilities*, I felt that was enough of a good thing and signed off the series of short books (as I thought) by indulging in something completely different – my fascination with time, time travel and science fiction – in the form of *Nine Musings on Time*. But other people had different ideas. In particular, our grandchildren began to ask deceptively simple questions, which required a great deal of thought to answer accurately. I realised that this was a reversal of the procedure I had used in tackling my series of three short books – instead of providing simple answers to big questions, I was giving them big answers to simple questions. And if they were asking those questions, maybe other people would be interested in the answers. So I began to put together ten of the questions (theirs) and answers (mine), with no intended theme except that they are all genuine questions that I have been asked by the younger members of the family over the past couple of years. As I planned the structure of the book, though, I realised that the questions form a natural progression in terms of the place of the Earth in the Universe, and the place of people on our planet, so that is more or less the order in which the answers appear here. The questions are, of course, originally much older than my inquisitors, and some of the answers are almost as old as the questions. But if you think you know the answers, you may be in for a surprise or two. Which to me is a feature of what Richard Feynman called 'the pleasure of finding things out'. Obvious questions do not always have obvious answers, which is part of the fun of science. I hope you have fun with these examples. If you do, make the most of them, because I have at present no plans to write a book called *Eleven Intriguing Possibilities*, not least because I cannot think of eleven suitable topics for discussion. But if you can think of any, feel free to send an email to john@gribbin.co.uk; one should never say 'never again'.

John Gribbin, June 2022

QUESTION

1

Why Is the Sky Dark at Night?

The obvious answer is that the side of the Earth that is experiencing night is turned away from the Sun, and we are looking out into the cold, dark Universe. But why is the Universe cold and dark apart from a sprinkling of stars? As far as we know, the first person to think seriously about this puzzle was the Englishman Thomas Digges, one of the inventors of the telescope. In 1576, Digges suggested that the Universe is infinitely big and infinitely old, rejecting the ancient idea of the Earth surrounded by a series of 'crystal spheres'. He realised that in an infinite Universe full of stars, you ought to see a star in every direction you looked, with no dark spaces in between, but he reasoned that the very distant stars were simply too faint to be seen. But in 1610, Johannes Kepler realised that this argument would not wash.

Kepler turned the argument on its head. He said that in an infinite Universe full of stars, you would indeed see a star in every direction, so the dark night sky must tell us that the Universe is not infinite. He said that there must be an edge, or wall, around the Universe, and when we look through the gaps between the stars, we are looking at that wall. This almost fits in with the modern idea that our Milky Way Galaxy is an island of stars floating in dark space. If you imagine standing in a small grove of trees, you can look out through the gaps between the trees to the outside world, but in an infinite forest, everywhere you look you will see a tree. Unfortunately for this analogy, there are other galaxies out there, so the whole argument can be brought up to date by saying that everywhere we look beyond the Milky Way, we should see another galaxy.* I shall continue to talk about stars, because that is the way the story developed, but bear in mind that the argument applies with equal force to a Universe full of galaxies.

The person who first expressed the puzzle clearly in scientific terms was the Swiss astronomer Jean-Philippe Loys de Chéseaux, in the 1740s. The big difference between his approach and earlier speculations was that he put real numbers into the calculation. He estimated the distances to stars by guessing that they were all the same actual brightness as the Sun and working out how far away they would have to be to look so faint. Then he worked out how big the disc of the Sun would look to

....
* Edmond Halley, of comet fame, also pondered on the puzzle of the dark night sky, in 1721, but like Digges, he simply thought that very distant stars were too faint to be seen.

us at those distances. Finally, he worked out that if stars were spread out more or less evenly through the Universe in the same density as they are in our part of the Universe, these discs would all be overlapping, so the entire sky would be as bright as the Sun, once we looked out to a distance equivalent, in modern terms, to 10^{15} (a million billion) light years. His conclusion was that either stars are not distributed evenly in this way – that there must be an 'edge' to our grove of astronomical trees – or that something happens to hide the light from very distant stars. De Chéseaux suggested that light gets fainter and fainter as it travels across space to us. He was wrong (or at least, partially wrong, as I shall explain), but at least he tried to explain the puzzle.

A modern update to de Chéseaux's argument makes it even more powerful for the mathematically inclined (if you are not mathematically inclined, skip this paragraph). Imagine the Earth at the centre of a large (potentially infinite) series of thin 'shells' (thin by astronomical standards, that is), like onion skins. If each shell is the same thickness, then at any distance r, the volume of a shell, is proportional to r^2.* If stars are distributed evenly through the Universe, the number of stars in each shell is proportional to the

---

* The volume is actually proportional to r^2 multiplied by the thickness of the shell, but since all the shells have the same thickness, that doesn't affect the calculation.

3

volume, so it also goes up as r^2. But the light we receive from each star goes down in proportion to r^2 (it is proportional to $1/r^2$). So the factors of r^2 cancel out, and every shell contributes the same brightness to the night (or day!) sky. Of course, some of the light from very distant shells gets blocked by stars in nearer shells, so once again, the sky should 'only' be as bright as the surface of the Sun.

De Chéseaux ought to have been the person who got his name attached to this scientific puzzle, but in fact it has gone down in history as 'Olbers' Paradox', which is doubly annoying because the German astronomer Heinrich Olbers did not think of it first, and it is not a paradox. But so it goes.

Olbers came up with his variation on the theme in 1823. It was very similar to de Chéseaux's idea, but he suggested that the light from distant stars doesn't just get tired on its way to us but is absorbed by dust in space. The snag, which he missed, is that if there is dust in space absorbing energy from the stars, the dust will heat up, eventually becoming as hot and bright as the stars themselves. So in an infinitely large, infinitely old Universe, the puzzle of the dark night sky still exists.

The first hint for the correct explanation of the puzzle came from the American writer Edgar Allen Poe, in an essay, 'Eureka', published in 1848. But this really was only a hint at a potential answer, in the middle of a lot of metaphysical musing (some good, some bad), and Poe does not deserve quite as much credit as he is sometimes given. Nevertheless, it is worth looking at the good bits of what he said, which, with hindsight, can be seen as pointing in the right direction.

He starts out well enough, clearly expressing the nature of the puzzle:

> A very slight inspection of the Heavens assures us that the stars have a certain general uniformity, equability, or equidistance, of distribution through that region of space in which, collectively, and in a roughly globular form, they are situated.

And:

> All observation of the firmament refutes – the conception of the absolute infinity of the Universe of stars.

But it soon becomes clear that he is refuting the idea of an infinity of stars, not an infinity of space.

He successfully points out that because light travels at a finite speed it takes a long time to travel across space to us from a distant star or from what he calls 'nebulae', which we now know to be other galaxies:

> Since the light by which we recognize the nebulæ now, must be merely that which left their surfaces a vast number of years ago, the processes at present

5

observed, or supposed to be observed, are, in fact, not processes now actually going on, but the phantoms of processes completed long in the Past.

This is an important insight. Because light travels at a finite speed, we see objects as they were when the light left them. Even light from the Sun takes just over eight minutes to reach us. So telescopes are in a sense time machines, giving us views of more ancient times the further out we look. With this understood, by isolating one passage in 'Eureka', Poe can be made to seem quite prescient:

> Were the succession of stars endless, then the background of the sky would present us an uniform luminosity, like that displayed by the Galaxy – *since there could be absolutely no point, in all that background, at which would not exist a star.* The only mode, therefore, in which, under such a state of affairs, we could comprehend the voids which our telescopes find in innumerable directions, would be by supposing the distance of the invisible background so immense that no ray from it has yet been able to reach us at all. That this *may* be so, who shall venture to deny?

Unfortunately, in the next sentence in his essay, without actually denying this, he says:

I maintain, simply, that we have not even the shadow
of a reason for believing that it *is* so.

If Poe had omitted that sentence, he could rightly have
been credited with the idea that the sky is dark at night
because the Universe is not old enough to have been filled
with starlight.

His own explanation of the puzzle of the dark night
sky comes a little later in the essay and echoes the ideas
of Kepler. Poe refers to:

Those frequent gaps in the Heavens, where our utmost
scrutiny can detect not only no stellar bodies, but no
indications of their existence: – where yawning chasms,
blacker than Erebus, seem to afford us glimpses,
through the boundary walls of the Universe of Stars,
into the illimitable Universe of Vacancy, beyond.

Which is simply the old idea of an isolated astronomical
grove with eternal emptiness beyond.

It was this idea of an eternity of space and time that
left the mystery of the dark night sky unexplained (and
largely ignored) until well into the 20th century. Things
started to change at the end of the 1920s, when the
Belgian cosmologist Georges Lemaître and the American
astronomer Edwin Hubble (with help from fellow
astronomer Milton Humason) independently discovered

Edgar Allan Poe
Unknown author; Restored by Yann Forget and Adam Cuerden,
Public domain, via Wikimedia Commons

that light from distant galaxies has been stretched to longer wavelengths on its way to us. This is the famous 'redshift', so-called because red light has longer wavelengths than blue light – more about this phenomenon in the answer to Question 2. It soon became established that this shift happens because space itself is expanding, or stretching, carrying galaxies away from one another. It is not a result of galaxies moving through space, but a stretching of space itself, in line with the equations of the general theory of relativity (which could have been used to predict the effect, but that is another story).

Lemaître pointed out that if the Universe is expanding in this way today, then long ago, all the stars in all the galaxies must have been squashed together in one lump at the beginning of the process of expansion, what we now call the Big Bang. Astronomers argued about whether there really had been a Big Bang up until the 1960s, when a combination of factors (one of which I will discuss shortly) provided clinching evidence in favour of the idea. Subsequent observations of the rate at which the galaxies are being carried apart, and other data, tell us that the Big Bang happened 13.8 billion years ago. What happened before that, if there was a 'before', is still up for debate. But the Universe as we know it is only 13.8 billion years old, so there cannot be any stars older than that, and there has not been enough time for the stars, even in an infinite Universe, to fill the sky with starlight.

But there is more. In the 1980s, the Austrian-born British cosmologist Hermann Bondi looked at the puzzle from a different perspective. Stars don't last for ever. They start out with a limited supply of energy (released by converting light elements such as hydrogen into heavier elements such as helium), and the life of a star is only a few thousand million years. The stars we see today are essentially made of hydrogen (and a little helium) left over from the Big Bang, and when all of their fuel is exhausted there will be no more starlight. The puzzle is turned on its head – not 'why is the sky dark at night?' but 'why isn't the sky completely dark at night?' The answer is still the same – the Universe is relatively young and has only been around for 13.8 billion years. There hasn't been time for all the hydrogen and helium fuel to have been used up in successive generations of stars, but when it is, the sky will be darker still.

Which brings me to the final twist in the tale, highlighted by British astronomer Edward Harrison in his book *Cosmology: The Science of the Universe*. He asked what it is that we actually see in the dark gaps between the stars. As he puts it, 'through the gaps between stars we look back to the beginning of the Universe', to the Big Bang itself. And what we see there is both the evidence for the Big Bang and the ultimate solution to the puzzle of the dark night sky.

As anyone who has used a hand pump to inflate a bicycle tyre knows, when things are compressed, they get hotter. The reverse is also true – an expanding gas cools down. This is the principle behind a domestic refrigerator. In the pipes inside a fridge, the working fluid is allowed to expand and cool down, chilling the air around it (it actually 'expands' from a liquid into a gas). In the pipework outside the cool compartment, the fluid is compressed (back into a liquid) by a pump and gets hot, but the heat is radiated away into the air, leaving cool fluid to go back inside. Then the fluid goes round for another cycle, in effect carrying heat from the inside of the refrigerator to the outside world. This is one aspect of a fundamental scientific law, described properly by the equations of thermodynamics, and it applies to the Universe at large as well as to domestic fridges. The Universe is expanding, so it must be getting colder. Which means that it used to be hotter in the past. And this also explained a puzzling discovery made by two American researchers, Arno Penzias and Robert Wilson, in 1962.

Penzias and Wilson had been preparing a radio telescope at Holmdel in New Jersey for a programme of research and were baffled to find a weak hiss of radio noise coming from all directions in space, between the stars and galaxies. The energy of radio waves can be described in terms of temperature, and the hiss they 'heard' had a temperature of about 3 Kelvin, −270° on the Celsius scale. They took the puzzle to a team at nearby Princeton University, headed by Jim Peebles, who realised that this must be radiation from the time when the whole Universe was young and hot – from the Big Bang itself.

At this point, I need to explain just what astronomers mean by the term Big Bang. Winding the expansion of the Universe back in time, using the equations of the general theory of relativity, implies that everything we can see in space burst out from a single point with zero volume, a singularity. Nobody believes that this is literally how the Universe as we know it began, not least since the laws of quantum physics prevent such things as singularities existing. The actual 'birth' of the Universe is still a mystery, but if we set that moment as time zero, we can describe what happened at different epochs as the Universe expanded away from something close to a singularity. The term 'Big Bang' properly refers not to the singularity, but to the time just after time zero, when the entire Universe was hot and dense.

The discovery of the background radiation became regarded as the moment when the Big Bang origin of the Universe became established as scientific fact, although actually, there was other important evidence in support of the idea which was discovered later in the 1960s. But this background radiation has now been studied in great detail and provides our best guide to what happened in the Big Bang. With improved observations of the background radiation from radio telescopes on the surface of the Earth, instruments hoisted high into the atmosphere by balloons, and detectors on satellites, combined with calculations based on the general theory of relativity, we know that roughly 300,000 years after time zero, the entire Universe was filled with material as hot as the surface of the Sun today, about 6,000 K. Before then, it was hotter still. This is not a coincidence. The visible surface of the Sun is at that temperature because it is just cool enough for negatively charged electrons to link up with positively charged nuclei to make neutral atoms. Under hotter conditions (inside the Sun, or earlier in the history of the Universe than 300,000 years after time zero), the electrically charged particles interact with light and other electromagnetic radiation, which gets bounced around from one charged particle to another; but once those particles are locked up in this way, the light can stream freely out across space. This happens at the surface of the Sun today, and it happened everywhere when the Universe cooled below the critical temperature and electrons became locked up in atoms. The light from the Big Bang then escaped from the clutches of matter and has been streaming across space unimpeded for 13.5 billion years, getting stretched to longer wavelengths as radio noise and cooling all the time as it does so. Which to some extent vindicates de Chéseaux, although the way the light from the Big Bang gets 'tired' on its journey across space does not fit his image of an eternal, unchanging Universe.

So there are two reasons why the sky is dark at night. Stars don't live long enough to heat up all the space between them, and the Universe is not only finite in time, it is getting cooler as it ages. Even in an infinitely large Universe, this would be the case. But this leads us to another question. When we 'look' at the background radiation in the Universe, we are looking back in time 13.5 billion years to the hot fireball of the Big Bang. But how far away is it? How far can we see across the expanding Universe?

QUESTION

How Far Away Are the Most Distant Things We Can See?*

I am paraphrasing the question I was asked, because the original version, 'How far can we see?', doesn't have a straightforward answer, as I shall explain. I don't mean how far can we see with the unaided human eye, but how far can astronomers 'see' using the best detectors available? Before I can answer that question, I need to remind you about a few details of the Big Bang in which the Universe as we know it was born, and in particular, go into a little more detail about the nature of the redshift phenomenon. I also need to remind you that a light year is a measure of distance – the distance light can travel in one year – not a measure of time. Astronomers usually prefer to measure distances in terms of units called parsecs, where one parsec is roughly 3.26 light years. Unfortunately, that can also cause confusion. In *Star Wars: A New Hope*, Han Solo describes having

....

* This answer is an expanded version of an article I wrote for the magazine *Popular Astronomy*.

'made the Kessel Run in less than twelve parsecs!' much to the amusement of astronomers, since like light years, a parsec is a measure of distance, not time. But I digress.

We know that there was a Big Bang for the reasons outlined in the previous answer. The most compelling evidence for the Big Bang, as I explained there, is the presence of the electromagnetic radiation reaching the Earth from all directions on the sky – the cosmic microwave background radiation, which derives from hot gas at a temperature about the same as that of the surface of the Sun today, and was emitted about 300,000 years after the Big Bang. As the Big Bang happened 13.8 billion years ago, that radiation has been travelling across space to us for very nearly 13.5 billion years. And since electromagnetic radiation travels at the speed of light, that must mean that those hot clouds are just about 13.5 billion light years away, must it not? Well, no, actually. During all the time the radiation has been on its way to us, the Universe has been expanding. So those clouds are now a lot farther away than this naive calculation suggests.

To avoid any misunderstanding, I should clear up any confusion about redshift and the Doppler effect. The Doppler effect, named after the Austrian mathematician Christian Andreas Doppler, is most familiar to us in the form of sound. The note of a siren on an emergency vehicle rushing towards us sounds higher in pitch than the sound of the same siren on the same vehicle rushing away from us, because when the vehicle is approaching, the sound waves get squashed together, and when it is receding, they get stretched out. Exactly the same sort of thing happens with light, but it only becomes noticeable when the light source is moving at a good fraction of the speed of light, which is 300,000 kilometres per second. This is very useful in astronomy. The key to the nomenclature is that blue light has shorter wavelengths than red light. Light from a star moving towards us is compressed, squashing the waves closer together and making the wavelength shorter, so features in the spectrum of that light move towards the blue end of the spectrum – a blueshift. We know how big this shift is, for any particular star, because the same features in the spectrum, called spectral lines, can be studied in the light from objects in laboratories on Earth, where there is no shift. Similarly, if the star is moving away from us, the light is stretched to longer wavelengths and features in the spectrum towards the red end of the spectrum – a redshift. In Doppler shift terms, for light, red means receding, blue means approaching. The size of these effects tell astronomers how fast stars are moving, and this is particularly useful when one star is going around another in a binary system, because knowing the speed the stars are moving, plus some basic laws of orbital motion, makes it possible to work out their masses.

The same sort of thing does actually happen with galaxies. Galaxies mostly occur in clusters, and they move about within clusters, like bees buzzing around in a swarm, because of their gravitational influence on one another. This produces a Doppler shift in the light from those galaxies. In one example close to home, light from the Andromeda Galaxy, which is in the same cluster as our Milky Way Galaxy, shows a blueshift, indicating that it is moving towards us at about 110 kilometres per second, and the two galaxies will interact ('collide' is too strong a term; the stars don't bump into each other, but pass by like two flocks of birds) in about 5 billion years.* But all of these effects are caused by things moving through space. I said in the previous answer that the cosmological redshift is a different phenomenon, caused by space itself stretching while the light is on its way to us. The longer the light has taken on its journey, the more space has expanded in that time and the more the light has been stretched. A useful analogy is with a spring stretched between two objects. If the objects move apart, the spring stretches, and the 'waves' it makes get stretched flatter. But the spring has not moved as a whole from one object to the other. The amount of 'flattening' depends on the stretching distance involved, so this makes the cosmological redshift a measure of distance, not of speed. But what distance is it measuring?

Imagine that you are standing somewhere in the middle of one of those long travelling walkways found in places such as

---

* It's all relative, of course. An observer in the Andromeda Galaxy would say that we are moving towards them at about 110 kilometres per second. Our galaxy is nothing special in cosmological terms.

airports, but the travellator has not been switched on. Mark the spot where you are standing with a blob of paint. I am standing at the end of the travellator, and when it is turned on the pavement starts to carry you away from me. But you walk briskly towards me, overcoming the speed of the walkway, and when you get to me, the travellator is turned off. By that time, the blob of paint is much farther away from me than it was when you set out. That is the 'proper distance' to the paint blob now, not the distance it was from me when you started walking. In order to calculate the proper distance to an object by measuring the redshift in the light from it, we need to use some very simple equations. People who write books like this are often told that adding even a couple of equations scares readers off and are advised to leave them out; but as the question I am answering was posed by someone who has not yet taken GCSE maths, and he didn't find the equations frightening, I am going to ignore that advice.

Cosmologists use the symbol z to refer to redshift, and the Greek symbol lambda (λ) to refer to wavelength. In a fairly obvious shorthand, λ_{obs} is the wavelength we observe (measure) for a particular spectral line in the light from a distant galaxy, and λ_{rest} is the wavelength measured for the same spectral line in light from an object at rest (not moving) in the laboratory. The value of z is defined in terms of how much the spectral lines are shifted towards the red. The great value of this parameter is that the distance to a galaxy is related to its redshift, so by measuring redshift,

19

cosmologists can work out how far away galaxies are; the bigger the redshift, the more distant a galaxy is. And it is relatively easy to measure. The cosmological redshift is equal to the observed wavelength of a particular line in the spectrum, minus the wavelength of the equivalent line for an object at rest in the laboratory, all divided by the 'rest' wavelength. In the standard notation:

$$z = \frac{\lambda_{obs} - \lambda_{rest}}{\lambda_{rest}}$$

A little rearrangement gives:

$$1 + z = \lambda_{obs}/\lambda_{rest}$$

This cosmological redshift combines with any Doppler effect in an individual galaxy. So when astronomers look at a cluster of galaxies, they will find an average redshift caused by the expansion of the Universe, carrying the whole cluster away from us, but some galaxies will have a slightly smaller redshift than the average, because they happen to be moving in our direction in the swarm and the Doppler effect is subtracting from the cosmological effect, while others will have a slightly higher redshift because they happen to be moving away from us in the swarm and the Doppler effect is adding to the cosmological effect. But for the distant objects I am interested in here, the Doppler effects are tiny compared with the cosmological redshift.

Converting a measurement of redshift into a measurement of distance depends on calibrating what is called 'the redshift – distance relation' using measurements of distances to the small number of galaxies whose distances can be measured in other ways. The most important of these distance indicators are exploding stars, called supernovae (more about supernovae in the answer to Question 5). There is one kind of supernova, called SN1a, which all explode with the same brightness. For obvious reasons, they are referred to as 'standard candles'. If one of these occurs in a distant galaxy, we can work out how far away that galaxy is by measuring how bright (or faint) the supernova looks to us. This is like having a long street illuminated by a series of lights that all have the same intrinsic brightness, another set of standard candles. If you knew how bright the lights were, you could, if so inclined, calculate the distance to each lamppost without leaving a spot at the end of the street by measuring the brightness of the light it carries. The calculations are slightly complicated by the need to use the equations of the general theory of relativity (which are a bit more advanced than GCSE maths, and which I won't include here) to work out how the rate at which the Universe is expanding has changed over cosmic time. This requires more subtle measurements of the redshift in the light from objects whose distances can be inferred using other techniques, including studies of supernovae. The bottom line is that there is good evidence that until recently, in cosmic time terms, the expansion of the Universe was slowing down, but now it seems to be speeding up. When the appropriate numbers are put into the cosmological equations, we find that the particles in the hot gas that emitted the cosmic background radiation are now about 45.7 billion light years away; that is their proper distance (also called the comoving radial distance). So that is as far as astronomers can 'see' today. The wavelengths of radiation from that time have been stretched from those of visible light to those of microwave radio waves, corresponding to a redshift of just over 1,000.

If we could detect the Big Bang itself (which might one day be possible using gravitational radiation, which also travels at the speed of light), we would be looking at something only a few hundred thousand years older than the background radiation, and only a correspondingly small extra distance away, at 46.6 billion light years. There are slight differences depending on which set of cosmological equations (which cosmological model) you prefer, but in round numbers, this tells us that the distance to the edge of the observable Universe is 46 billion light years. That defines the cosmological horizon (also called the comoving horizon, or the particle horizon). This is as far as we can see in any direction, the radius of the bubble of space that we can observe, so that bubble is about 92 billion light years across.

The comoving horizon is the farthest distance from which we can receive information today. But it does not mean that

SN 2013cu (iPTF13ast)

SDSS, prior to supernova explosion   Palomar

Gal-Yam et al. 2014; Nature, May 22, 2014

Supernova
Avishay Gal-Yam, Weizmann Institute of Science

we are at the centre of the Universe, any more than the existence of a visible horizon for people on board a ship somewhere in the Pacific Ocean means that the ship is at the centre of the ocean. As with mariners in the Pacific, an observer near the edge of 'our' bubble would be able to see as far as us in our direction, and the same distance in the opposite direction beyond our horizon. If there were any observers looking in our direction from near the edge of our horizon, however, they would not see the Milky Way as it is today, but as it was nearly 13.8 billion years ago – they would detect the cosmic background radiation from the clouds of hot gas from which galaxies, stars, planets and ourselves would eventually form. And unlike the horizon seen from a ship in the Pacific Ocean, the cosmological horizon continues to move outward as the Universe expands – the 'travellator' has not stopped moving.

There is, however, another horizon that limits what even the most technologically advanced future civilisation would ever be able to see. This is the cosmic event horizon, and it is defined as the farthest distance from us now from which light being emitted today will ever reach us (sometimes called 'the future visibility limit'). This is about 61 billion light years. Anything farther away from us will be carried away by the expansion of the Universe faster than the speed of light, so no information from that region will ever reach us, just as no information, or light, can escape from a black hole. The present cosmological horizon is at about three-quarters of this distance. Leaving aside any practical problems of observation, this means that the total number of galaxies that will ever be detectable from Earth is only about twice the number already observed.

Even this is not the end of the story. If the expansion of the Universe is indeed accelerating at present, as observations suggest, and the acceleration continues indefinitely, even the galaxies we see today will fade away as they become increasingly redshifted – the light waves will become stretched flat. Everything with redshifts in the range from five to ten today will be invisible within 4 to 6 billion years, roughly by the time the Sun, nearing the end of its life, swells up and becomes a red giant. If life is now just getting started on a planet like the Earth orbiting a star like the Sun, and evolution proceeds at the same pace there as it has on Earth, by the time there is a civilisation on that planet capable of studying the Universe at large, there will be a lot less for them to study, no matter how good their telescopes are. Their night sky will be even darker than ours.

All of which brings me back to where I started this story, and to a pet hate. When astronomers identify the distance to extremely remote objects, that distance is often widely misrepresented. For example, there is an object called GRB 09423, produced by a burst of gamma rays in a cosmic explosion detected in 2009 in a galaxy at a redshift of 8.1. This object is one of the many that will be undetectable when the Sun is a red giant. Although redshift is used as a standard measure of distance, for such large redshifts it is better interpreted as a measure of how close in time the event was to the Big Bang. The gamma-ray burst's redshift implies that it occurred about 13.2 billion years ago. So the popular media (and some naughty professional astronomers) interpreted this as meaning a distance of 13.2 billion light years. In fact, the object is now about 32 billion light years away (and a little bit farther away now than what it was in 2009).*

With that off my chest, the answer to Question 2 is straightforward. In the words of the song 'On a Clear Day, You Can See Forever', the truth is rather more prosaic, but also more intriguing. The background radiation we can 'see' is 46 billion light years away and started out as hot as the surface of the Sun today. Which leads us to the next question. Or rather, a pair of questions: How old is the Sun, and how does the Sun keep shining so brightly, 13.8 billion years after the Big Bang? I have merged the answers to these questions together in the next chapter.

....

* I have no hope of persuading the world at large to change their habits in this regard, but I trust that you will now be wary of falling into this trap. If, however, you want to correct such mistakes for yourself when you see misleading announcements of record-breaking redshifts in lesser publications, check out this nifty online resource, Ned Wright's 'proper distance calculator': www.astro.ucla.edu/~wright/ ACC.html. This allows you to set all the relevant factors; then leave all other figures as they are shown and just change the value of z for an object and click on 'General' to get its age after the Big Bang.

How Old Is the Sun?

The age of the Sun must, of course, be more than the age of the Earth, which adds another layer to this question, as well as the puzzle of how the Sun stays hot. This also relates to the answer to Question 1, and the fact that stars like the Sun are very old (by human standards) in turn leads to the answer to Question 5; but that will have to wait. All of which shows, though, how trying to answer the simplest question can lead to profound insights into the nature of life, the Universe and everything.

Before the 19th century, most people in the Christian world believed that the Earth and Sun had been created about 6,000 years ago. This was based on a completely unscientific calculation that involved counting back the generations referred to in the Bible from Jesus Christ to Adam and Eve. But as soon as scientists began to under-stand the processes that shaped the Earth, they realised that the timescale involved must be much longer than this.

The first dramatic step in the right direction proved to be such a huge leap that the scientist who came up with it, the Frenchman Jean-Baptiste Joseph Fourier, never actually published it, presumably for fear of being ridiculed. Fourier picked up on the idea, which went back to Isaac Newton, that the Earth had formed as a molten ball of rock and had since been steadily cooling down. This seemed the logical way to explain our planet's volcanic activity, and offered a way to work out how long it would have taken for the Earth to cool to its present state. Fourier used equations that describe how heat flows through different substances, made allowance for the fact that once a crust of solid rock formed it would act like a blanket, slowing down the escape of heat from the interior, and suggested that the temperature at the centre of the Earth must be about 6,000° Celsius, the temperature of molten rock. In 1820, he wrote down the formula that gave the age of the Earth based on all this. But he never wrote down (at least, not for public consumption) the number that comes out of the formula. It is 100 million years – some 16,000 times more than the Biblical estimate. It took 40 years before anyone else did essentially the same calculation, getting essentially the same answer, and published the result. But by then, in the second half of the 19th century, there was serious scientific concern that even 100 million years was far too short a time to explain the appearance of the Earth, and the variety of life on it today.

Late in the 18th century, a Scottish geologist, James Hutton, tackled the question of the age of the Earth (and by implication the age of the Sun) from the other direction – outside in, rather than inside out. He studied surface features of our planet, from the slow process of erosion, carving features of the landscape, such as river gorges, to the way geological strata have been buckled and twisted by immense forces operating over long intervals of time. He reached the conclusion that the age of the Earth was so immense that it could not be calculated. He wrote: 'We find no vestige of a beginning – no prospect of an end.' Hutton's own writings didn't make much impact, because of his dense style, but in 1802, his friend John Playfair published an edited version of Hutton's text that got a lot of attention and started a debate about the age of the Earth. The stage was set for the next major contributor to the story, another Scot, Charles Lyell, who was born in 1797.

Lyell came from a wealthy family and was sent to Oxford to study law. But some time in the middle of the second decade of the 19th century, when he was about eighteen, he picked up a book about geology in his father's library and became fascinated by it. This led him to Playfair's version of Hutton's work, and alongside his law studies, he began attending lectures on mineralogy. Although Lyell did qualify as a lawyer, in the 1820s, he went on a tour of Europe and saw first-hand how the landscape has been moulded by geological activity. He was particularly impressed by the layers of volcanic rock, separated by layers of sedimentary rock, which showed how Mount Etna had built itself up over a very long time. Back in England, he wrote a great book in three volumes. The title of this masterwork was simply *Principles of Geology*, but the subtitle gave more than a hint of the contents: *Being an Attempt to Explain the Former Changes of the Earth's Surface by Reference to Causes now in Operation*.

Lyell's contention was that the activity we see around us today, such as erosion, volcanism and earthquakes, are all that is needed to explain how the planet got to be the way it is, provided there has been enough time. There is no need for catastrophes such as the Biblical Flood. The first volume of Lyell's book was published in 1830, and at the end of the following year, a copy was among the library carried by a young geologist, Charles Darwin, when he set off on a voyage around the world on HMS *Beagle*. When Darwin later developed the idea of evolution by natural selection, he realised that the process required an immense amount of time to produce the diversity of life on Earth today, and he eagerly accepted the evidence put forward by Lyell, who, Darwin wrote, had given him 'the gift of time'. But in the second half of the 19th century, after the publication of his book *On the Origin of Species* in 1859, all of this brought Darwin and the geologists – Lyell had endorsed Darwin's ideas in a major new edition of *Principles of Geology* that was published in 1865 – into serious scientific conflict with the astronomers and physicists who said that it was impossible for the Sun to be as old as their theories required.

In Britain, the most outspoken opponent of the idea of a long timescale like the one proposed by Darwin and Lyell was the physicist William Thomson, who later became Lord Kelvin. By this time, astronomers had a good estimate of the mass of the Sun, from studies of the orbits of the planets held in the Sun's gravitational grip. Using this number, Thompson pointed out that even if the Sun were entirely made of coal, burning in an atmosphere of pure oxygen, it would burn out in a few thousand years. This was his way of highlighting that no processes known to be going on Earth could keep the Sun hot for long; but even Thomson agreed that it must be older than this simple calculation implied. The question was, how old?

Thomson spent many years refining an idea about how to keep the Sun shining that jumped off from the growing understanding of the relationships between different kinds of energy that went hand in hand with the industrial revolution, powered by coal and driven by steam. The key point is that energy cannot be created or destroyed. It can only be converted from one form into another. At a scientific meeting held in 1853, Thomson learned of an idea proposed by an obscure researcher, John Waterston. Waterston was obscure because he was not part of the scientific establishment and had trouble getting his ideas published, but at least this one fell on

Lord Kelvin
ETH Library, public domain, via Wikimedia Commons

fertile ground. He had realised that if a lump of rock in space fell towards the Sun, it would go faster as gravitational potential energy was converted into kinetic energy, then when it hit the Sun, all the kinetic energy would be dissipated as heat. Could a steady rain of these 'meteorites' explain how the Sun stays hot? Alas, no.

Thomson tried to make the idea work but realised that it would require an impossibly large supply of space rocks. To highlight this, he calculated how much energy would be supplied if each of the planets fell into the Sun in turn. Mercury, for example, could provide enough energy to keep the Sun shining for seven years, and Venus enough for 84 years; but even Neptune, the most distant large planet in the Solar System, could only provide enough energy to keep the Sun shining for about 2,000 years. Thomson's brilliant solution to this puzzle wasn't completed until the 1880s, but I shall skip the intervening steps and cut to the chase. He realised that the important thing in the calculation was not the size of the individual space rocks, but the total mass (amount of matter) involved. Two half-Suns bashing together would generate as much heat as a cloud of meteorites (or pebbles, or grains of sand) adding up to the mass of the Sun would release if they fell together. Even if you started with a huge cloud of gas with the mass of the Sun, and it fell together under its own weight, it would generate the same amount of heat. By the time the cloud had shrunk

33

to the size of the Sun, the temperature at its heart would be millions of degrees Celsius. The pressure generated by all the hot particles bouncing around in the core of the star would then stop it collapsing. This is an excellent way to start a star shining, and astronomers are sure that it is indeed how the Sun and stars got started. But Thomson went a step further. He realised that once a star had formed as a glowing ball of gas, if it cooled off a little bit, it would start to shrink. But the shrinking would release more gravitational energy, warming it up again. And he calculated that if the Sun was shrinking at a rate of 50 metres per year, far too small for 19th-century astronomers to measure, it would shine with a steady glow. But for how long?

In an early calculation, based on the energy stored in a spread-out cloud of gas with the mass of the Sun, Thomson had estimated that the available gravitational energy was enough to keep the Sun shining for a few tens of millions of years, and concluded that it was 'on the whole most probable that the sun has not illuminated the earth for 100,000,000 years ... As for the future, we may say, with equal certainty, that inhabitants of the earth cannot continue to enjoy the light and heat essential to their life, for many million years longer, unless sources now unknown to us are prepared in the great storehouse of creation'. Although he did not intend it that way, this comment proved remarkably prescient. With hindsight, we can see that the conflict between the astronomical timescale and the timescale required by geology and evolution was indeed telling us that there must be sources of energy unknown to Victorian science. But this still seemed a ridiculous idea to physicists in the 1890s, when Kelvin came up with his final estimate for the age of the Sun, taking on board the idea of a slow shrinking, of 24 million years. The German physicist Hermann Helmholtz came up with the same result independently, and this is now known to astronomers as the 'Kelvin–Helmholtz timescale' for stellar collapse.

Before I tell you about the source of energy that was unknown to 19th-century science (which you have probably guessed now, anyway), and what it means for the age of the Sun, it is worth looking at how much (or, from another perspective, how little) energy is actually needed to keep the Sun shining. My favourite analogy comes from a book by George Gamow, *A Star Called the Sun*, published in 1964. Gamow started by asking his readers to guess how long it would take to bring a pot of coffee to the boil if each cubic centimetre of the liquid in the pot generated heat at the same rate as the average rate heat is produced by each cubic centimetre of the Sun. His eye-opening answer was that it would take months for the pot to boil. The Sun is huge, and to account for the rate at which heat is escaping from its surface, on average, each gram of material releases just under one-half of

35

one ten-millionth of a calorie of heat each second. This is much less than the rate at which heat is produced by your body, through chemical processes. The point Gamow was making, of course, is that the production of heat is not spread out evenly through the Sun. Most of the energy is released in a small volume at its heart, and none in the much more voluminous region outside the core. And the first hints of the source of this energy came in the 1890s, exactly at the time Kelvin was putting the finishing touches to his (and Helmholtz's) timescale.

The German Wilhelm Röntgen discovered X-rays by accident in 1895 (the discovery was announced on 1 January 1896) when he was doing some experiments with electricity. Dramatic though the discovery was, it did not require any new source of energy, because the energy came from the beams of 'cathode rays' (electrons) used in the experiments. But when Frenchman Henri Becquerel was following up this work in February 1896, he discovered that some form of radiation could be produced by certain substances, including compounds of uranium, even when they were wrapped in thick black paper and had no outside source of energy. This newly discovered form of radiation penetrated the paper and left its mark on photographic plates. Following Becquerel's discovery, Marie Curie and her husband Pierre began investigating radioactivity, as it became known, and discovered two 'new' radioactive elements, polonium and radium, before the end of the century. By 1903, Pierre Curie and his assistant Albert Laborde had made accurate measurements of the amount of heat released by radium. The amount astonished their colleagues. A single gram of radium produces enough heat to raise the temperature of 1.3 grams of water from freezing point to boiling point in one hour – and it does this hour after hour, with no sign of stopping. But what source of energy was providing the heat?

Even without knowing the source of the energy, in 1903, the English astronomer William Wilson suggested that radioactivity could be a source of heat for the Sun – Gamow's coffee-pot analogy shows how little radium you would need, spread through the volume of the Sun. Wilson calculated that all that would be needed was 3.6 grams of radium in each cubic metre of the volume of the Sun. George Darwin (one of Charles Darwin's sons) picked up this idea and suggested that this might resolve the conflict between the evolutionary timescale and the astronomical timescale. He was wrong, but on the right track (and, incidentally, radioactive heating does help to explain why the interior of the Earth is still hot long after the planet formed, greatly extending the timescale calculated by Fourier). By 1904, the New Zealand-born physicist Ernest Rutherford and his colleagues had shown that the energy is released when atoms of one element are converted into atoms of another element, with particles being emitted in the process. This is known as radioactive decay. Radium does indeed stop releasing energy when all its atoms have been used up in this way, but that takes a very long time.

In a presentation that year to the Royal Institution in London, Rutherford pointed out that radioactive heating could be the 'sources now unknown to us' referred to by Kelvin decades before. Kelvin, who was in the audience, was delighted. But Rutherford was only partly correct. Just a year later, the first step towards a proper understanding of what keeps the Sun hot was taken by a young physicist working in Switzerland – Albert Einstein.

Einstein had no idea that he was solving the puzzle of the age of the Sun when he came up with his special theory of relativity in 1905. It is the special theory that gives us the most widely known equation in the whole of science, $E = mc^2$. This tells us that matter (mass, m) is a form of energy (E), and that they are interchangeable. The speed of light (c), is a huge number, so a little mass is equivalent to a lot of energy. In radioactive decay, an atom of a substance such as radium emits one or more particles and is converted into an atom of another element. The combined mass of the remnant atom and the particles released is slightly less than the mass of the original atom, and the 'missing' mass is in the form of energy that shows up as the kinetic energy of the particles, appearing as heat. But a different process, also involving the conversion of mass into energy, takes place in the heart of the Sun.

It took more than 30 years* for astrophysicists to work out exactly how the conversion of mass into energy provides the heat to keep the Sun shining, but the process involves atoms of hydrogen (strictly speaking, their nuclei) fusing together to make atoms (nuclei) of helium. Each helium nucleus is 'made' from four hydrogen nuclei, and the mass of the helium nucleus is slightly less than the mass of four hydrogen nuclei added together, with the extra mass being liberated in the form energy that keeps the heart of the Sun hot. There is enough hydrogen in the Sun to keep this process going for roughly 10 billion years, ample time for evolution to do its work. But on that evidence alone, the Sun might be a billion years old, or nine billion, or anywhere in between. The clue to its actual age comes, once again, from radioactivity.

Each radioactive substance 'decays' into what are known as its daughter products on a regular timescale. For some radioactive elements, the timescale is very short, and they disappear almost literally in a puff of smoke. But for others it is very long – billions of years. The rates can be found from studies of radioactive decay in the lab, without waiting for billions of years. This provides

---

* As I described in my book *Seven Pillars of Science*.

the basis for radioactive dating of rocks. If you start with a pure sample of a particular radioactive element, such as uranium, the atoms will be steadily converted into atoms of another element, in this case lead – actually, as the American chemist Bertram Boltwood worked out in the early 20th century, uranium decays into radium and the radium then decays into lead, but the principle is the same. As time passes, the proportion of uranium goes down and the proportion of lead goes up. So if you come across a piece of rock containing uranium and lead, you can work out the age of the rock by measuring the proportions of the two elements. This technique was established by Arthur Holmes, in England, in the first two decades of the 20th century. The oldest rocks found on Earth are those that were meteorites, lumps of rock from space left over from the birth of the Solar System. This dating technique, using measurements of radioactive rubidium and its daughter strontium, tells us that the oldest of these space rocks formed about 4.5 billion years ago. So we know that the Solar System, including the Earth and the Sun, is about 4.5 billion years old, and the Sun has so far used up about half of its supply of nuclear fuel.

This seems like a satisfactory answer to the question 'how old is the Sun?', but it is built on the foundations of Einstein's famous equation. Which prompted one of my inquisitors to ask: 'How do we know Einstein was right?' Read on!

How Do We Know Einstein Was Right?

Einstein's discovery that mass and energy are interchangeable came from his special theory of relativity, published in 1905. The theory is 'special' in the sense that it is a special case because it only deals with the behaviour of things moving in straight lines at constant speed (that is, at constant velocity) relative to one another. Einstein's famous equation does not actually appear in that paper, because he only realised this implication of his theory after that paper had been sent off for publication. So the equation first appears, in a slightly different notation, in another paper published later the same year, which is a kind of postscript, or coda, to the first paper. In a letter to his friend Conrad Habicht, written in September 1905, Einstein described how the idea came to him:

> One more consequence of the electrodynamics paper has also crossed my mind. Namely, the relativity principle, together with Maxwell's equations [of electromagnetism], requires that mass be a direct measure of the energy contained in a body. Light carries mass with it. With the case of radium

there should be a noticeable reduction of mass. The thought is amusing and seductive.

As he put it in the published paper: 'The mass of a body is a measure of its energy content.'

This also works the other way round. The Sun stays hot by converting mass into other forms of energy, but other forms of energy can be converted into mass. If you kick a ball, most of the extra energy goes into making the ball move faster; but a little goes into making the ball a little more massive. For things moving much more slowly than light, the increase in mass is far too small to notice. But if Einstein was right, for things that move at a sizeable fraction of the speed of light the balance changes. Then, if you kick the object a large amount of the extra energy goes into making it more massive, and a smaller proportion goes into making it go faster, so it only speeds up a little bit. This all emerged from the special theory.

It was another ten years before Einstein came up with a more general theory that also deals with the behaviour of objects that are being accelerated – including, crucially, accelerations caused by gravity.* Logically enough,

* Acceleration can mean a change in speed or a change in direction, or both. So a satellite in orbit around the Earth, for example, is being accelerated by gravity because it is constantly changing direction, whether or not its speed changes.

this became known as the general theory of relativity, and it includes the special theory within itself, so any proof that the general theory is correct is also proof that the special theory is correct. It is the theories that are 'special' or 'general', not the relativity, so it is never correct to refer to the 'theory of special relativity' or 'the theory of general relativity'.

Until Einstein came along, the best theory of gravity that physicists had was the one developed by Isaac Newton in the 17th century. But they knew that Newton's theory wasn't perfect, because it could not explain an odd detail about the orbit of the planet Mercury around the Sun. Like other planets in the Solar System, the orbit of Mars is an ellipse, with the Sun at one focus of the ellipse. It is very nearly circular, but if you imagine exaggerating the shape it would be like a single petal of a simple drawing of a daisy. But each time Mercury goes round the Sun, the orbit shifts slightly sideways, like sliding round from one daisy petal to the next. This slippage is called the shift in the perihelion of the orbit, and although it is tiny it could not be accounted for by Newton's theory. Astronomers speculated that it might be caused by a planet inside the orbit of Mercury tugging on Mercury, but they could find no trace of such a planet. The theory Einstein developed in 1915, however, predicted exactly the size of the measured effect. He wrote to a colleague that he 'was beside myself with joyous excitement' when he made the calculation,

43

and told another that 'the results of Mercury's perihelion movement fills me with great satisfaction'.* This was impressive evidence that Einstein (or rather, Einstein's general theory) was right. But explaining something that has already been discovered is never quite as impressive as predicting something that is only discovered after the prediction is made. And that was the next, and most famous, proof of the general theory.

Einstein had reported his explanation (not really a prediction) of the perihelion shift of Mercury in a lecture to the Prussian Academy of Sciences in November 1915.† In the same lecture (!), he made a genuine prediction. Newton's theory predicted that light passing close by the Sun would be bent by the Sun's gravity; Einstein's equations agreed that the light would be bent, but he predicted an effect twice as big as the one predicted by Newton's theory. Here was a way to make a direct comparison between the predictions of the two theories, if only there was a way to measure how light from a distant star got bent when it passed by the edge of the Sun. Fortunately, there was.

Usually, it is impossible to see, or photograph, the light from a distant star passing close by the edge of the Sun,

---

* Quoted by Walter Isaacson, *Einstein: His Life and Universe*, Simon & Schuster, 2007.
† Details are given in my book *Einstein's Masterwork: 1915 and the General Theory of Relativity*, Icon, 2015.

because of the glare from the Sun itself. But during an eclipse of the Sun, when sunlight is blocked out by the Moon, the stars close to the Sun on the sky (but much further away, of course) become visible and can be photographed. By great good fortune, there was a solar eclipse in May 1919, and there was just time after the end of hostilities during the First World War for the British to organise a pair of expeditions to observe the eclipse, one from Brazil and one from the island of Principe, off the west coast of Africa just north of the equator. Photographs of the pattern of stars around the position of the Sun on the sky could then be compared with photographs of the stars in the same patch of the sky taken previously from other sites in the opposite season (around November), when the Sun was on the opposite side of the Earth, so those stars were in the night sky. The comparison showed that the stars nearest to the Sun seemed to be shifted slightly sideways at the time of the eclipse, because of the light-bending effect. And the size of the effect matched the prediction of the general theory, not the prediction of Newton's theory. The results were announced at a specially arranged joint meeting of the Royal Society and the Royal Astronomical Society in London in November 1919, and made headlines around the world. This was the beginning of Einstein's status as the most famous scientist in the world.

Since then, the light-bending phenomenon has become an important tool of astronomy to probe the furthest reaches of the Universe. The more mass you have, the bigger the bending effect can be, and some of the largest concentrations of mass in the Universe are clusters of galaxies, where, as well as the bright stars we can see, the cluster is filled with 'dark matter', whose presence is revealed by its gravitational effects. These clusters act like giant lenses, which magnify and distort the light from even more distant objects, such as single galaxies, that would otherwise be too far away and too faint to be seen with terrestrial telescopes. In one striking example, the gravity of a galaxy cluster dubbed RCS2 032727-132623 (the numbers are the coordinates of its position on the sky) has bent and amplified the light from a much more distant galaxy. Early in the 21st century, the images this produced were analysed by a team from the University of Chicago; many popular accounts of this discovery said that the distant galaxy is 10 billion light years from Earth, but what they mean is that the light we see it by left 10 billion years ago. As I explained in the answer to Question 2, that galaxy is now a lot further away. But in this case that doesn't matter. What is important is that thanks to gravitational lensing we are able to see a galaxy as it was when the Universe was young, less than 4 billion years after the Big Bang. The galaxy has been studied using the Very Large Telescope (yes, that really is its name) in Chile, and imaged by the Hubble Space Telescope.

Michael Gladders, one of the members of the Chicago team, emphasised that 'what's happening here is a manifestation of general relativity [*sic*]; Instead of seeing the normal, faint image of that distant source, you see highly distorted, highly magnified, and in this case, multiple images of the source caused by the intervening gravitational mass'.

Using a computer program that 'reversed' the distortions caused by gravitational lensing – which depends on understanding Einstein's theory – the team constructed an image of the galaxy as it would appear if we had a telescope powerful enough to see it directly. This revealed regions where stars are (or were) being born, showing up as bright points of light. These star-forming regions are much brighter than any star-formation region in our Milky Way, providing astrophysicists with insights into how stars and galaxies form. Gravitational lensing doesn't just provide proof that Einstein was right; it is now a tool used routinely by astronomers, who don't question the accuracy of Einstein's equations any more than you might question whether the Sun is going to rise tomorrow.

So Einstein (or Einstein's theory) is definitely right. But there is one last beautiful piece of evidence that directly confirms the accuracy of the most famous equation in science. Physicists can actually measure the amount of mass equivalent to a certain amount of energy.

This develops from machines invented in the 1930s to probe the structure of matter – the archetypal 'atom

This graphic shows a reconstruction (*at lower left*) of the bright galaxy, whose image has been distorted by the gravity of a distant galaxy cluster. The small rectangle in the centre shows the location of the background galaxy on the sky if the intervening galaxy cluster were not there. The rounded outlines show distinct, distorted images of the background galaxy resulting from lensing by the mass in the cluster. The image at lower left is a reconstruction of what the lensed galaxy would look like in the absence of the cluster, based on a model of the cluster's mass distribution derived from studying the distorted galaxy images.

NASA, ESA, J. Rigby (NASA Goddard Space Flight Center),
K. Sharon (Kavli Institute for Cosmological Physics, University of Chicago),
M. Gladders and E. Wuyts (University of Chicago)

smashers'. Relativity theory (special or general) describes the behaviour of things moving relative to one another – hence the name. For the example I want to use here, this means that we are entitled to regard ourselves as stationary ('in a stationary frame of reference', or 'at rest', in physicists' jargon) and use Einstein's equations to describe the behaviour of fast-moving particles in laboratories here on Earth. Those fast-moving particles are things such as electrons and protons, which have electric charge so they can be manipulated using electric and magnetic fields, and the labs are places like Fermilab in Chicago and the European Organization for Nuclear Research (CERN) in Geneva.

The first particle accelerators were straight tubes, with a vacuum inside, down which the particles were accelerated. The fast-moving particles were directed at targets made of different materials, triggering reactions that revealed details of the structure of atomic nuclei. Faster is better, in this case, because faster particles carry more energy and have a bigger effect on their targets. But these linear accelerators had a major drawback because the speed of the particles was limited by the length of the tube down which they were being pushed by electromagnetic fields. To get around this problem, at the beginning of the 1930s, Ernest Lawrence, working at the University of California, Berkeley, invented a new kind of particle accelerator, which became known as a cyclotron. As the name implies, a cyclotron accelerates charged particles round a curved path – not a circle, but outwards from the centre of a flat cylindrical vacuum chamber, following a spiral path until they emerge as a powerful beam from a point near the circumference of the chamber. The particles are held in this spiral trajectory by a steady magnetic field, and accelerated by a varying electric field that is tuned to give them a kick every time they go round the loop. This makes it possible to accelerate the particles to higher energies than in a linear accelerator because they go round the loop many times.

The frequency at which a particle goes round the loop (circling in a perpendicular magnetic field), and receives a kick, is called the cyclotron frequency; it depends on the charge and mass of the particle, and the strength of the magnetic field. Rather neatly, for a particular mass as the particles spiral outward, the rotation frequency stays constant, because the particles are travelling faster over a longer distance, round a bigger circle. So the frequency of the kick provided by the electric field stays the same and the beam continues to accelerate. But this sets a limit on how fast the particles can go. Once they are going at a sizeable fraction of the speed of light, the extra energy they receive from each kick by the electric field doesn't simply go into making them move faster; it makes them more massive. But the cyclotron frequency depends on the mass, so they get out of step with the varying electric field. This is unfortunate because the extra mass is a measure of how much more energy they are carrying, so even if the speed doesn't increase by much, they pack a more powerful punch when they hit the target, which is what the experimenters want. Or rather, they would pack a bigger punch, provided there was a way to keep accelerating them as their mass increased. That was the next trick the experimenters came up with.

By the late 1930s, cyclotrons had started to reach the limit of the energy they could put into beams of particles. As particles reached relativistic speeds and their effective mass increased, the cyclotron frequency for a given electric field had to change if it was to keep kicking the particles. One way to solve this problem was to decrease the frequency of the field kicking the particles round the loop as the particles spiralled outwards and their mass increased, to keep it synchronised with the changing orbital frequency of the particles in the loop. One of the first machines based on this principle – a synchrocyclotron – was built by Lawrence's team in 1946. These were the most powerful accelerators during the 1950s. They have since been superseded by other designs, but all that is relevant here is that the way the frequency of the electric field has to be tweaked to keep it synchronised with the particles as their mass increases exactly matches the mass increase predicted by Einstein's equations. There is no doubt at all that Einstein was right, and that E does indeed equal mc^2; which is a key factor in answering the next question.

Where Did Everything Come From?

I need to qualify this question. From the context, the person who asked me meant: 'Where does planet Earth and everything on it come from?' So that is the question I shall attempt to answer for her. And for the purposes of this answer, I shall start from the well-established cosmological evidence that the Big Bang produced a mixture of about 75 per cent hydrogen and 25 per cent helium, from which the first stars formed.* So the first part of the answer concerns the origin of all the other chemical elements from which things like planets are made.

As I explained in the answer to Question 3, a star like the Sun keeps hot by converting hydrogen into helium in its core. This is a multi-step process, but the result is that each time this happens, four protons (hydrogen nuclei) are converted into a single helium nucleus, which consists of two protons and two neutrons. For obvious reasons, this is called

---

* See Ian Morison's book *Introduction to Astronomy and Cosmology* if you want the nitty-gritty. These percentages are in terms of mass.

helium-4. Neutrons are like protons in terms of mass but have no electric charge. Protons have positive charge, and in the process of helium formation the extra charge is got rid of in the form of positrons, a kind of positively charged electron. Overall, when four hydrogen nuclei combine to form one helium nucleus, just over 0.7 per cent of the mass of the original four protons is released as energy.

The helium nucleus is a particularly stable entity, and it is also known as an alpha particle. For the Sun, and stars with about the same mass as the Sun, this is the end of the story. When all the available hydrogen has been converted into helium, the star will cool down into a stellar cinder known as a white dwarf. But for stars with a few times more mass than the Sun, when the hydrogen is used up, the star shrinks a little, gets hotter thanks to the Kelvin–Helmholtz effect, and the pressure inside triggers further reactions, based on building up more elements by fusing alpha particles with one another and with successively more complex nuclei. Each step releases energy and keeps the star hot – up to a point.

The first nucleus that could be made by fusing two alpha particles together would be beryllium-8, but this is unstable and very little beryllium builds up inside stars. Fortunately for us, though, during its short lifetime, a beryllium-8 nucleus can fuse with a third alpha particle to make stable carbon-12, so stars make plenty of carbon. From there on, the process of adding alpha particles produces oxygen-16, neon-20, magnesium-24, silicon-28, and so on. The heaviest elements that can be produced in this way are iron and nickel; forcing nuclei to fuse into even heavier elements requires an input of energy, as I shall explain. Intermediate elements are produced in more modest quantities when these main nuclei absorb or emit single particles such as protons or electrons. But one of these intermediate elements is produced in relative profusion. A series of particle interactions starting with carbon converts some carbon nuclei into stable nitrogen-15.

As a result of all this, apart from helium, which does not get involved in chemical reactions (as opposed to nuclear reactions) the four most common elements in stellar material are hydrogen, carbon, nitrogen and oxygen. These are also the four most common elements found in living things – so important to biology that they are collectively referred to by the acronym CHON.* Life is clearly based on the elements that are made inside stars – as the song says, we are stardust. But how does this star stuff get out of the stars to make planets, and people?

The story really begins at the point where the release of energy by nuclear fusion stops, although there are hints of what is to come earlier in the life cycles of stars. The steps higher up the chain of fusion involving alpha particles only

....

* No mystic significance should be read into this. Life has simply made use of the most common materials available.

happen inside stars that have more than about eight times as much mass as the Sun, which is why there is so much carbon, oxygen and nitrogen in stardust. Stars with a few times more mass than the Sun go through a phase in which the heat from their interiors makes their outer regions swell up enormously, so they become what are known as red giant stars. At this stage of its life, material from deep inside a red giant is dredged up to the surface. It typically becomes hundreds of times bigger in diameter than the Sun, and at the surface of such a star, the pull of gravity is extremely feeble, so a lot of stuff escapes in the form of a 'stellar wind', which carries away not just individual atoms but molecules such as carbon monoxide and even more complex compounds, which are identified by astronomers using spectroscopy. A star can easily lose one-tenth of its solar mass of material in this way every thousand years – a mass equivalent to 33,000 times the mass of the Earth. But this is tiny compared with what is scattered by stars that start life with more than eight times the mass of the Sun.

What happens then depends on how much mass is left over when all the nuclear 'fuel' is exhausted. A stable white dwarf must have less than about 1.4 times the mass of the Sun to settle down into a quiet old age; any more than that and it collapses under its own weight, releasing a huge amount of gravitational energy. If a white dwarf starts out with a bit less than this critical limit, it can suck in more matter by its gravitational attraction, especially if it has a companion star at the red giant stage, and increase its mass. As soon as the mass reaches this limit, the star collapses, and the energy released sends a wave of fusion sweeping through the star as it explodes, producing all the elements up to iron (iron-56, to be precise) and spreading them into interstellar space. There is nothing left behind. This is known as a Type I Supernova. But even this is modest compared with the fate of a star with more than about fifteen times the mass of the Sun.

These stars go through successive stages of nuclear burning, until they end their lives with a core of iron (the size of the Earth but with the mass of the Sun), surrounded by shells, like onion skins, containing elements such as silicon, carbon and oxygen, and helium, with an atmosphere of hydrogen. When their fuel is exhausted, the core collapses even more dramatically than a collapsing white dwarf, forming either a neutron star (with the mass of the Sun in a ball about ten kilometres across) or a black hole. This sends a blast of energy outward through the outer layers. The energy involved makes all the elements heavier than iron and spreads the mixture out into space.* This is a Type II Supernova.

---

* Some very heavy elements are produced in even more exotic events involving colliding black holes, but the details need not worry us here.

All these processes spread elements heavier than helium out into space, seeding the clouds of gas (mostly still hydrogen and helium) between the stars, and providing the raw material from which new stars form. But it is a very slow process, by human standards. From a variety of evidence, astronomers estimate that about ten solar masses of material condenses to form new stars in our Milky Way Galaxy each year, and is replaced by recycled material from previous generations of stars. Most stars are a bit smaller than the Sun, so this means that among the hundreds of billions of stars in the Milky Way, between ten and twenty genuinely new stars light up each year. But the galaxy has been around for at least 10 billion years, and over that time, more than a hundred billion stars have been formed in this way – about a third of all the stars in our galaxy today. The rest were formed in what is known as 'starburst' activity when the galaxy was young – such starburst galaxies, active long ago, have been identified at high redshift by the light that left them a few billion years after the Big Bang, as I mentioned in the previous chapter.

All this explains where the chemical elements that make up the Earth and ourselves were made, and how they got spread between the stars. But how did some of that material coalesce to form our Solar System?

The evidence from radioactivity tells us that the Solar System formed a bit more than 4.5 billion years ago, when the Milky Way, judging from other astronomical evidence, was already at least 5 billion years old. So by then there was plenty of 'stardust', spread by previous generations of red giants and supernovas, in the clouds of gas between the stars from which new systems formed. Such clouds are still around, and still forming stars, today, so astronomers have been able to study the process in some detail, combining observations of things like the Orion Nebula, a star-forming region in the constellation Orion, with their understanding of the laws of physics. It begins when a cloud roughly twenty parsecs (about 65 light years) across, containing a third of a million solar masses of material is squeezed by interactions with its neighbours, perhaps including the explosion of a nearby supernova, and starts to collapse.

At the time the cloud in which our Solar System formed collapsed, it was still made up mostly of hydrogen (70 per cent) and helium (27 per cent) with 1 per cent oxygen, 0.3 per cent carbon, 0.1 per cent nitrogen and just a smattering of other elements. But much of the more interesting material was not in the form of gas, but locked up in dust grains and ices, including quite complex molecules.* As the giant molecular cloud collapsed, it fragmented and broke up into blobs, within which

----

* I described this interstellar chemistry in *Seven Pillars of Science*.

Star-forming region of Orion
ESO, Mark J. McCaughrean

individual stars formed, just as we see in Orion today. The blob from which our Solar System formed probably started out with about two solar masses of material. Inevitably, individual blobs like this must be rotating, and as our blob shrank it span faster and faster, like a spinning ice skater tucking in their arms. By the time the growing centre of the blob had become small enough and hot enough to shine through the Kelvin–Helmholtz effect, it was surrounded by a rotating fat disc of dust and gas (like a ring donut), while the central proto-star continued to grow as it pulled in more material – and at the same time, gas far away from the young star was blown away into space by its increasing warmth. Discs like this have been seen around many young stars. But by the time the central star had grown to the size of the Sun today, all the excess gas had been blown away, nuclear fusion reactions had started in its interior, and the tiny fraction of dusty material left after the gas had gone had settled down into a thinner disc, more like the rings of Saturn. What happened to the stuff in that disc depended on how far the material was from the Sun.

Working outwards from the Sun, there are four small, rocky planets (Mercury, Venus, Earth and Mars), then a belt of rocky debris, followed by four giant, gassy planets (Jupiter, Saturn, Uranus and Neptune), then a belt of icy debris, including Pluto, which used to be classified as a planet, but isn't even the biggest of these icy lumps. It is easy to explain the reason for the separation between the rocky material of the inner Solar System and the icy material of the outer Solar System. Close to the hot young Sun, icy material (not just water ice, but also things like frozen ammonia) would have evaporated and the molecules blown further out from the central star. But beyond a certain point, the temperature would have been low enough for ices to stick around and accumulate into giant planets. The critical region where the temperature starts to be low enough for ices to be stable lies between the orbits of Mars and Jupiter and is referred to by astronomers as the snowline. What happens beyond the snowline is fascinating in its own right,* but not important in the story of where the Earth came from, except for one thing that may have been worrying you. If all the ices inside the snowline evaporated and were blown away, how come the Earth is covered in water today? This is because comets, icy visitors from the outer regions of the Solar System, carried water and other volatile material into the inner Solar System after the planets formed, and some of these comets struck the young Earth, depositing not only water but other volatile material and some of the complex molecules that have been identified in molecular clouds on the young planet (including the precursors of life).

....

* As I describe in *The Reason Why*.

Within the snowline, dust grains in the disc collided and stuck together, gradually forming lumps big enough to attract other lumps by gravity. The grains may have been particularly sticky because heat from radioactivity had partly melted some of them. Samples from meteorites, which are pieces of rock left over from the planet-building process, contain elements that are the daughters of highly radioactive elements, which were themselves short-lived, and must have been produced in a supernova explosion nearby just before the planets formed. Whatever the details of the mechanism, the precursors of planets grew rapidly. Using computer simulations of this process, astronomers estimate that within a million years from the time the Sun switched on, there may have been as many as 30 large rocky lumps orbiting the Sun in the region out to the present-day orbit of Mars. Some were as small as the Moon (which has 27 per cent of the diameter of the Earth) and some as big as Mars (53 per cent of the diameter of the Earth). These large objects were surrounded by a swarm of smaller objects, which they swept up in a series of collisions, and collided with each other, merging until only five large planetary objects were left.

Five? You may think I have made a mistake, but I haven't. As well as proto-Mercury, proto-Venus, proto-Earth and proto-Mars, there must have been one other object about the size of Mars. And it is thanks to that other object that we are here to ask questions like 'where do we come from?'

If you have read my book *Eight Improbable Possibilities*, you will know where we are going. But for new readers, here is a brief summary: Our planet is unique in the Solar System in having a Moon that is roughly a quarter the size (in terms of diameter) of the planet. To an unbiased observer from another planet, the Earth–Moon system would look more like a double planet than a planet plus a moon. But that super-large Moon didn't get there just by being captured by the young Earth. Studies of the composition of lunar material and simulations of the dynamics of the young Solar System provide a compelling picture of how the Moon formed.

When the Earth itself formed it would have been molten, but the surface quickly cooled down to form a thick, rocky crust, with its share of heavy metals such as iron settling into the centre. The planet Venus today provides an idea of what the Earth would look like if nothing else had happened to it. But within a few million years (no more than 10) of the Earth itself forming, it was struck a glancing blow by the rogue Mars-sized proto-planet – astronomers are so sure this existed that they have given it a name, Theia, after the mother of the Moon goddess, Selene. This impact would have re-melted both Earth and Theia, with lighter materials from the crust of both splashing out into space, while their iron-rich cores merged and settled into the centre of the Earth. The excess crustal material formed a ring around the Earth from which the Moon formed in the same way that the planets formed around the Sun. As the Earth cooled, water and other volatiles were dumped on it by comets to make the ocean and atmosphere, together with complex molecules that may have kick-started life. And that is where everything came from, although it is not the end of the story of the Earth.

Beneath that atmosphere and ocean, the planet was left both with a large molten-iron core (responsible, among other things, for its magnetic field) and a very thin solid crust, which got broken into pieces called plates that were pushed around the surface by the convective motion of the fluids beneath the surface. Which brings me to our next question.

QUESTION

How Fast Do Continents Move?

Anyone who has looked at an image of the Earth from space might have noticed the way the bulge of Africa seems to fit the gap between North and South America, with Brazil nestling underneath. In fact, you don't need images from space to see this – once accurate maps of the continents became available, a few people noticed the 'co-incidence' and speculated on its cause. The idea that the continents had once been joined and were split apart in some great catastrophe gained wider currency in the second half of the 19th century, after the Italian-American Antonio Snider-Pellegrini published a book on the subject entitled *The Creation and its Mysteries Unveiled*, in 1858 (the year Charles Darwin and Alfred Russel Wallace presented their theory of evolution by natural selection to the Linnean Society). Although they rejected the idea of a single catastrophe linked to the Biblical Flood, an increasing number of scientists accepted the evidence that South America and Africa had once been joined, which began to build up from a variety of sources.

67

Some of this evidence relates to the work of Darwin and Wallace. The kinds of plants and animals found on opposite sides of the Atlantic at similar latitudes resemble one another, although because living things evolve, the match is not perfect. A better match comes from the rocks. Mountain ranges that disappear into the sea on one side of the ocean reappear on the other side, as do the geological strata and the fossils they contain. The analogy that is often made is that if you took a single sheet of newspaper and cut it into the shapes of Africa and South America before pulling the pieces apart, you would still be able to read the lines of newsprint across the gap between them. By the end of the 19th century, it was clear that the continents had once been joined. The questions that remained to be answered were how they had become separated, and how long had it taken – how fast did the continents move?

In 1908, in a presentation to the Geological Society of America, Frank Taylor, of Stanford University, described 'continental drift' (as it became known) as a 'mighty creeping movement', and drew attention to the discovery of a great undersea mountain range, the Mid-Atlantic Ridge, that lies roughly halfway between Europe and North America and extends south between Africa and South America. He was the first person to suggest that this is the place where the continents divided, and that it 'has remained unmoved while the two continents on opposite sides of it have crept away in nearly parallel and opposite directions'. Nobody took much notice of Taylor's ideas at the time, but he turned out to be very much on the right track. The person whose ideas about continental drift eventually got a lot of notice was a German meteorologist, Alfred Wegener, although it turned out that he was not entirely on the right track.

Wegener was not a geologist, but he knew enough geology to be annoyed by a scientific paper that he came across in 1911 that claimed that the similarities between things on opposite sides of the ocean could be explained if there had once been a 'land bridge' joining them, which had sunk beneath the waves. This had to be nonsense, because even in the early years of the 20th century, it was known that the crust of the continents is less dense than the crust of the oceans, so that continents would float on the denser ocean floor rocks in a way similar to the way ice floats on water. If you push an ice cube below the surface of a glass of water, it bobs up again as soon as you let go, and the same thing would happen to a land mass that was somehow pushed down into the oceanic crust.

Wegener was so annoyed that although he didn't give up the day job, he spent the rest of his life (he died in 1930) developing and promoting his version of the idea of continental drift. And he knew a lot about floating ice because he had worked as the meteorologist on a Danish expedition to Greenland, where he had seen how floating ice sheets can break apart and move though the water, but do not sink beneath the waves. Unfortunately, although he was right in thinking that land bridges could not sink, what he knew about floating ice led him down a false trail as he developed his ideas over the next two decades.

But first, what Wegener got right. He assembled a huge weight of evidence to show that the continents had moved. He was the person who came up with the newsprint analogy, and as a meteorologist he was able to use fossil evidence to reconstruct past climates and show, among other things, that the island of Spitzbergen, which now lies to the north of the Arctic Circle, had once been in the tropics, and covered by lush vegetation. All this, and other evidence, enabled him to reconstruct a time when all the present-day continents had been joined in one land mass, a supercontinent which he called Pangea, meaning 'whole Earth'.* He estimated that Pangea had begun to break apart about 300 million years ago,† and he explained mountain ranges existing as a result of collisions between continents, or, as in the case of the Rockies and the Andes, crumpling of continents at the leading edge of their motion. But he could not explain how the

....

* The name Gea, or Gaia, is now familiar from Jim Lovelock's theory of the living Earth.
† Modern estimates suggest Pangea formed approximately 335 million years ago and began to break up about 200 million years ago.

continents moved, and this was crucial in preventing his ideas gaining widespread acceptance.

What Wegener got wrong stemmed from his knowledge of floating ice. But even there, he very nearly got it right. Wegener suggested that the continents move through the oceanic crust of the sea floor the way a block of ice moves through the water if you give it a push. The image is like a great iceberg being moved through the water by the wind blowing on its bulk. But as Wegener himself might have realised, when a sheet of floating iced breaks up and the pieces drift along, they are not moving through the water. Rather, they are being carried along by the ocean currents. Similarly, continents are actually being carried along by 'currents' in the oceanic crust, not moving through the oceanic crust at all. But the key evidence that explained this only began to become available a quarter of a century after Wegener died.

By the 1950s, the world was very different from the world Wegener knew. Following the Second World War, it had divided into two armed camps, confronting each other in the Cold War. In the West, one of the major concerns of the US military was that the Soviet Union might be able to hide submarines, equipped with nuclear weapons, in the depths of the Pacific Ocean. As part of the response to this perceived threat, in 1955, the US Navy commissioned a survey of the sea bed off the west coast of North America, using sonar to provide a map showing any features where submarines might try to hide. As part of the cover for this military work, scientists were allowed to carry out their own experiments during the survey, provided these did not interfere with the mapping. They decided, just out of curiosity with no preconceived ideas about what they might find, to measure the magnetism of the sea floor rocks, by towing an instrument called a magnetometer along behind their ship as it went back and forth across a patch of ocean, like a tractor going back and forth across a field as it ploughs. What they found was completely unexpected.

When molten rock solidifies, it picks up a trace of magnetism from the Earth's magnetic field, and this gets frozen into the rocks, as a kind of fossil trace of the magnetism around the rocks as it was setting. It starts off oriented north–south, but as the rocks get jumbled about by geological activity, such as earthquakes, the magnetism of a particular piece of rock might end up oriented in any direction. As far as they had any expectations, that is what the survey team thought they might find – a jumble of magnetic patterns in the rocks under the sea, with different rocks oriented in different directions. What they actually found was a pattern of very distinct stripes, running north–south. In one stripe, the rock magnetism was oriented north–south in the same sense as the present-day magnetic field of the Earth. In the next stripe, the pattern was reversed, running south–north, opposite to the present-day terrestrial magnetic field. The pattern repeated like the stripes on a barcode, with some stripes wider than others. The results of the initial survey were published in 1958 and triggered a wave of similar studies around the world, which led to an even more dramatic discovery.

Remember the Mid-Atlantic Ridge that Frank Taylor tried to draw attention to back in 1908? The surveys showed that the pattern of wide and narrow magnetic stripes (the magnetic barcode) is the same on either side of the ridge, and indeed the same symmetry is found on either side of similar ridges in other oceans. In one particularly striking example,* in the mid-1960s, a US research ship, the *Eltanin*, carried out a magnetic survey along a 4,000-kilometre-long track running East–West across the Pacific Ridge, to the south of Easter Island. The results of the survey – the wide and narrow magnetic stripes – were plotted on a paper chart with the ridge at the centre, and when the chart was folded in half along the line of the ridge, the two 'barcodes' sat on top of each other, each stripe on top of its counterpart from the other side of the ridge, highlighting the symmetry of the pattern of magnetic reversals.

---

* Which I mention because I remember reading about it at the time.

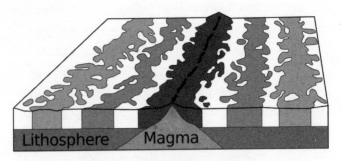

Oceanic 'barcode' magnetic stripes
Chmee2, Public domain, via Wikimedia Commons

Once the pattern had been noticed, it was straightforward to explain it. The ocean ridges are literally cracks in the Earth's crust, places where molten rock is welling up from below and pushing out on either side of the ridge, cooling as it does so and freezing in the magnetic field that is prevailing at the time. Taylor was right. The Mid-Atlantic Ridge is indeed the crack in the crust that split Europe and North America apart, and the resulting sea-floor spreading has been pushing them further apart ever since. Continents do not move through the rock of the sea floor but are carried on the back of plates of rock, like ice floes carried on ocean currents, which gives the concept of continental drift its modern name, plate tectonics.

None of this, though, means that the Earth is getting bigger as the oceans expand. Sea-floor spreading occurs at ocean ridges, but in other places the sea floor is being destroyed, pushed back under the continents. This is possible because the oceanic crust is both denser and thinner than continental crust. The results are particularly noticeable down the western side of the Pacific Ocean, where the effect of oceanic crust being pushed under the continent has produced great mountain ranges and volcanic activity – the islands of Japan have been entirely produced by this process. The Pacific Ocean is shrinking at the same rate that the Atlantic Ocean is expanding.

But how long does all this take? How fast do the continents move? Geologists know, from magnetic studies of rock strata on land, that the Earth's magnetic field is not constant, but reverses from time to time, with the north and south magnetic poles changing places. This does not mean that the Earth is toppling over in space; the magnetic field is produced by swirling currents of molten material deep in the interior (more of this in the answer to Question 7), and sometimes it dies away to nothing then builds up again in the opposite sense. Nobody knows why or how this happens, but the fact that it does gives geologists a very useful tool. In particular, they can use it to measure the ages of the magnetic stripes on the sea floor.

It's all possible because although many rock formations get jumbled up by earthquakes and other activity, there are some places where the strata lie neatly on top of each other, with the youngest at the top. The ages of the different layers of rock can be worked out using standard geological techniques, and when the magnetism of the rocks is measured, it reveals the same kind of pattern of broad and narrow stripes, corresponding to magnetic reversals, seen on the sea floor. But this time, the pattern makes a kind of calendar, extending backwards in time.

One of the things this tells geophysicists is how the orientation of the continents has changed as time passes. The pattern might show, for example, that at a certain time in the geological past, what is now Africa was turned at an angle to its present-day position. Combined with the fossil evidence of flora and fauna, to reconstruct climates of the past the way Wegener did, this enables geophysicists to work out not only when Pangea existed, but also when the pieces broke apart, and how they were carried around the globe by plate tectonics to their present positions. Geophysicists were able to put all this together in the late 1960s, as more powerful scientific computers became available, to produce maps showing the pattern of the continents at different geological times. By chance, I was one of the first people to see those maps of continental drift.

It happened because in those days a 'powerful' scientific computer had a memory of 128k,* occupied a large, air-conditioned room and was tended by a team of computer operators who fed it data in the form of punched cards and magnetic tape, and then collected output, often in the form of numbers and diagrams printed on paper. There were no visual display units; the output was only ever seen on paper, although it also existed on punched cards and so on. One such machine, an IBM 360/44, was owned by the Institute of Theoretical Astronomy (as it then was) in Cambridge, where I was a research student and had a part-time job as a computer operator.

. . . .

* That is not a misprint. 128,000 bytes. A modern smartphone may have a memory of 128 gigabytes, a million times as much as the best scientific computer in Europe in 1968.

The geophysicists who worked in a nearby building had an arrangement allowing them to run their programs on our machine, and one of my jobs was to collect their printed output ready for them to pick up. This printed output included those first maps of continental drift. So I saw them hot off the printer, and before they were seen even by the people responsible for the research, let alone appear in scientific journals. What I didn't appreciate at the time, though, was that all of this is still going on – that the Atlantic Ocean is getting wider even as I write these words.

This brings us back to the connection between the magnetic stripes on the sea floor and the magnetic patterns found in continental rocks. The pattern of broad and narrow stripes is very distinctive because the reversals of the magnetic field do not recur in a regular way. So it is possible to pick out a single stripe (and its mirror-image counterpart on the other side of the Mid-Atlantic Ridge) and say that it was laid down over a certain interval of geological time a definite number of millions of years ago. From that, it is a simple matter to calculate how fast the Atlantic has been widening over the past few tens of millions of years. On each side of the rift, new oceanic crust is being pushed away at a rate of just under two centimetres per year – so overall, the ocean is growing wider at a rate of nearly four centimetres per year. America is now more than two metres further away from

Europe than it was when I looked at those maps of continental drift being printed by the computer in Cambridge. To put this in perspective, new ocean crust is being laid down roughly at the same rate that your fingernails grow. So every time you cut your nails, remember that since the previous manicure, the continent has moved as far as the amount of nail removed.

This is all sound, secure science. But it does depend on understanding how oceans are formed, what fossil magnetism is and how magnetism of rocks in continents can be dated and related to the magnetism of rocks on the sea floor. It would be nice if there were some way to measure this movement directly. As it happens, there is – or rather, there are two ways to measure continental drift directly.

The first is accurate but may seem a little esoteric to anyone except a radio astronomer. Astronomers have a technique called radio interferometry among the tools they use to study distant stars and galaxies. It depends on using widely separated radio telescopes to study the same object at the same time and mixing the radio waves (letting them interfere) in a way that, among other things, reveals the difference in time between the waves arriving at each telescope. The time difference, of course, is related to the distance between the telescopes. Using telescopes in North America and in Europe in the late 20th century, radio astronomers

Man with long fingernails, c. 1906
Public domain, via Wikimedia Commons

monitored the radio waves from a distant quasar for more than ten years and found that Europe and North America are indeed still moving apart at just the rate inferred from the geophysical studies.

The other technique is even more direct. It simply involves bouncing laser beams from one ground station off a satellite equipped with bright reflectors, picking up the reflection at another ground station far away, then bouncing it back where it came from. The time taken for the round trip (along two sides of a triangle) directly indicates the distance between the two ground stations, the base of the triangle. This technique shows that the Pacific crust is moving westward at four centimetres per year, so it is disappearing under Asia at that rate, exactly balancing the growth of the Atlantic crust. Which answers the question 'how fast do the continents move?', but leads to another: What lies beneath the crust of the Earth?

QUESTION

7*

What Is Inside the Earth?

The question 'what lies beneath our feet?' is linked to another question – 'how do we know what lies beneath our feet?' Today, the answer to the second question seems obvious – by studying earthquakes. But using earthquakes to tell us what is inside the Earth is far from simple. Edward Bullard, an eminent Cambridge geophysicist, who produced the first computer fit of the continents from either side of the Atlantic, once told me that trying to work out the inner structure of the Earth by studying the vibrations from earthquakes (seismic waves) is like trying to work out the inner structure of a grand piano by listening to the noise it makes when it is pushed down a flight of stairs. But the process is made slightly easier because there is some other evidence to point the way.

....

* This answer is adapted from a section in our book *Planet Earth: A Beginner's Guide*, Oneworld, 2011, because I couldn't say it any better.

Physicists can work out the mass of the Earth by measuring the strength of its gravitational field, and they also know how big it is, so they know its overall density. This is bigger than the density of rocks at the surface of our planet, so to make the sums add up there must be a core of much denser material inside the Earth. The first person to make this calculation was Emil Weichert, a German geophysicist working in the 1890s. He inferred that the Earth has an iron core with a diameter 0.779 times the diameter of the planet and a density of 8.21 grams per cubic centimetre, compared with the density of 3.2 grams per cubic centimetre for the outer layer of the Earth, known as the mantle. These figures are pretty close to modern estimates.

Weichert also suggested that this prediction could be tested by studying how seismic waves travel through the Earth from the site of an earthquake to be detected far away.* In the very year he suggested this, 1897, an earthquake in India set a British geologist, Richard Oldham, thinking along the same lines.

Oldham was working for the Geological Survey of India, which was then under British rule. A major

....

* Which brings up a pet hate of mine. The epicentre is the point on the Earth's surface directly above an earthquake that occurs below ground; all well and good. But my hate is that the term has been hijacked by people who use it when they simply mean 'centre'. Rant over, thank you.

earthquake in Assam was felt over an area of a quarter of a million square miles, and by comparing measurements of the time it was felt from widely separated places, Oldham worked out that there must be three kinds of seismic waves, which travel through the Earth at different speeds.

One kind, called pressure waves (or P-waves) are like sound waves, and move with a push-pull motion. They are like the push-pull waves you can make with the toy called a Slinky, which is like a long spring. The other important kind of waves for studying the interior of the Earth are called shear waves (or S-waves), because they move with a to-and-fro sideways motion, like a snake, or the waves you can make by sending ripples running along a rope. Since P-waves travel faster than S-waves, they arrive first at detectors, called seismographs, or seismometers, and for that reason, the initial 'P' in P-wave is sometimes taken to mean 'primary'. Shear waves arrive second, so the 'S' in S-wave can also stand for 'secondary'.

In the body of the Earth, P-waves travel at speeds between about seven kilometres per second and fourteen kilometres per second (four miles per second and eight miles per second), while S-waves travel at speeds between about four kilometres per second and eight kilometres per second (2.5 miles per second and five miles per second). As a rule of thumb, in a given kind of rock, the S-wave travels at 60 per cent of the speed of the P-wave. P-waves can travel through both liquids

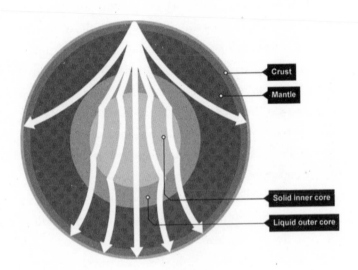

P-waves
USGS

S-waves
USGS

and solids, but S-waves cannot travel through liquids. It was the discovery that P-waves can travel through some regions of the interior of our planet where S-waves cannot travel that revealed the molten outer core of the Earth.

There are also surface waves, which, as their name implies, travel across the surface of the Earth. These can be very powerful and do a great deal of damage, but they do not tell us much about the deep interior of the Earth. That information comes from P- and S-waves, together known as body waves. Oldham settled in Britain in 1903 and studied data from thousands of earthquakes around the world, which among other things directly revealed the existence of the core.

This was possible because the seismic waves travel through the interior of the Earth at different speeds depending on what kind of rock they are travelling through. Among other things, the speed at which they move depends on the temperature of the rock, and whether that rock is soft or hard. As the waves travel through different kinds of rock, or the same kind of rock at different temperatures, the direction they are moving in can change, a bit like the way the direction of a beam of light can change when it moves from one kind of material (such as air) into another kind of material (such as glass, or water). This is called refraction. Also, when a seismic wave travelling through one kind of rock arrives at a boundary with a different kind of rock, it can be reflected, like light being reflected from a mirror.

Oldham's study implied that the core must be liquid, but in 1936, Inge Lehmann, a Danish geophysicist, found that the Earth has a solid inner core, which reflects seismic waves. But like the study of continental drift, the details of the inner structure of our planet were only worked out as a result of Cold War politics.

If you only had one seismometer with which to study earthquake vibrations, you really wouldn't be able to make much more sense of them than a person would be able to make sense of the noise made by a grand piano being pushed down a flight of stairs. But after the testing of nuclear bombs in the atmosphere was banned in the early 1960s, the military establishment and governments of the superpowers wanted to monitor the seismic waves from underground tests being carried out by their rivals. This led to the establishment by the US government of the Worldwide Standardised Seismic Network, or WSSN, which gathers data from seismic stations all over the world to be analysed at a central laboratory in the United States. This is still the most important network of this kind, but there are now hundreds of sensitive seismometers, linked together in networks that are spread over a large part of the surface of the Earth, and every day there are many small earthquakes going off somewhere, creating vibrations that can be picked up by those instruments and analysed.

Global networks are good at giving a broad picture of the structure of the Earth, especially its division into different layers. But there are also networks where many seismographs are placed more closely together to get a more detailed picture of what is going on in one particular region of the globe. The smallest details they can 'see' are on a scale of a few kilometres. Together, these techniques give geophysicists a picture of what is happening deep beneath our feet.

The rigid outer shell of the Earth – the lithosphere – is broken up into seven large plates and several smaller plates. Some plates are made entirely of oceanic crust, but others are made up of both oceanic and continental crust. No plate can move independently, because whatever it does affects its neighbours, and whatever they do affects their neighbours, and so on.

Beneath the crust, which is a bit like the shell of an egg, the interior of the Earth resembles the interior of the egg itself, with a core (corresponding to the yolk) surrounded by a deep layer of material (corresponding to the white of the egg). But unlike the yolk and white of an egg, these main layers of the Earth's interior are each divided into an inner region and an outer region, identified from seismic studies.

Starting at the surface and working downwards, towards the centre of the Earth, the crust is, on average, about seven kilometres (four miles) thick under the oceans and about 35 kilometres (twenty miles) thick on the continents. It makes up just 0.6 per cent of the volume of the Earth, and 0.4 per cent of its mass. The base of the crust is marked by a boundary called the Mohorovičić discontinuity (or Moho), after the Croatian scientist who discovered it. The main layer below the crust is called the mantle and is divided into two parts, the upper mantle and the lower mantle.

But the transition from the crust to the mantle is not a neat dividing line. The top of the mantle is a solid, rocky region that, together with the crust, is called the lithosphere; it extends down to a depth of about 250 kilometres (150 miles) below the continents, but it is much thinner under the oceans and little thicker than the crust itself at mid-ocean ridges. Just below the lithosphere, there is a semi-liquid region, a little more than 100 kilometres (60 miles) thick, still chemically part of the mantle – this is the asthenosphere. This part of the mantle is the key to plate tectonics. Because the asthenosphere is semi-liquid, the solid lithosphere above, including the crust, can slide about on it, allowing plates to move, the sea floor to spread and continents to drift. The plates that are the feature of plate tectonics don't just consist of crust but are slabs of rock that include both crust and the top of the upper mantle. Including the lithosphere and the asthenosphere, the upper mantle extends down to about 670 kilometres (415 miles) from the surface, and the lower mantle goes down to about 2,900 kilometres (1,800 miles). It makes up 82 per cent of the volume of the Earth, and 67 per cent of its mass. P-waves travel at about eight kilometres per second in the top of the mantle, and at nearly fourteen kilometres (8.5 miles) per second at its base.

At this depth, there is a much more dramatic transition to a region of liquid material, through which S-waves cannot pass, called the outer core. At the base of the outer core, about 5,100 kilometres, or 3,100 miles, below the surface of the Earth, we reach the top of the inner core, a solid lump of material some 2,400 kilometres, or 1,500 miles, across, about two-thirds the diameter of the Moon. One curious feature of the solid inner core is that it is rotating slightly faster than the rest of the Earth and has gained one-tenth of a rotation in the past 30 years, a rate of a little more than one degree per year, that is, 1/360 of a circle. The whole core is almost exactly the same size as the planet Mars. But both parts of the core, the seismic studies reveal, are much more dense than the mantle above. The core has a bit more than half the radius of the Earth, but less than one-fifth of its volume, because volume depends on the cube of the radius (for example, 2 cubed is 8 so a sphere with exactly half the radius would have only one-eighth of the volume). Altogether, the distance from the surface to the centre of the Earth is 6,371 kilometres, or 3,959 miles.

All of these distances are averages. The depths of the various boundaries are slightly different in different places, and they may change as time passes. In particular, the solid inner core is thought to be growing slowly, as part of the liquid outer core crystallises on top of it. This is one source of the energy that keeps the interior of our planet hot (along with radioactive energy), because when liquids solidify, they give out energy, called latent heat. So far, about 4 per cent of the core has crystallised, and it will take another 4 billion years or so for the rest to solidify. The whole core occupies only 17.4 per cent of the volume of the Earth, but contains 32.6 per cent of its mass, an indication of its very high density compared with the rest of our planet – about twelve grams per cubic centimetre (0.4 pounds per cubic inch), which is twelve times the density of water, and a little more than the density of lead in any of the forms in which you may find it on the surface of the Earth.

Plate tectonics is driven by convection in the mantle – or mantles. This sounds crazy: isn't the mantle solid rock, through which S-waves can travel? Indeed, if the mantle is shaken suddenly by an earthquake, vibrations can travel through it, like sound waves travelling through a ringing bell. But push it steadily for a long time and it will gradually flow like a very sticky liquid. There is actually something we use in everyday life that behaves like this – glass. If you hit a piece of glass with a hammer, it will shatter, like a solid. But if you look carefully at the stained glass in old cathedral windows, you will see that it is thicker at the bottom than at the top. This is because over the centuries since the glass was installed, it has flowed slowly downwards, like very sticky syrup, under the pull of gravity. The mantle is like glass, but even stickier.

Because of the division of the mantle into upper and lower regions, separated by a narrow boundary that has been revealed by seismic surveys, nobody is quite sure how this convection works. One possibility is that the two parts of the mantle each have their own convective system, like a double boiler, one on top of the other. The opposite extreme would be if the whole mantle con-vects as a single unit, more or less ignoring the boundary between the upper and lower mantle. But the best expla-nation seems to involve a bit of both of these ideas. Slabs of sea floor that have been forced downward by subduc-tion can be traced by seismic scans all the way down to the boundary between the upper and lower mantles at a depth of about 650 kilometres (400 miles). Once there, they seem to spread out in a layer that collects for per-haps hundreds of millions of years, before it piles up so much that it breaks through the boundary and carries on into the lower mantle, like an avalanche, almost all of the way down to the top of the outer core. There is some seismic evidence that solid slabs of material accumulate at the base of the mantle, where it may take as long as a billion years for the heat from the core to warm them suf-ficiently to make the material start rising back towards the surface. The reheated material then becomes part of a rising plume that breaks right through the boundary into the upper mantle and forms a hot spot. There is one under Hawaii, and another, under the East African Rift, that is cracking the African continent apart and separating most of Africa from Asia. If this process continues, it will produce a new ocean with its own mid-ocean ridge.

The heat that drives these plumes upward and is the primary cause of sea-floor spreading comes all the way from the bottom of the mantle, lifting a column nearly 3,000 kilometres (1,800 miles) high. All this is possible only because the interior of the Earth is hotter than its surface. And we know exactly how hot the core is because we know exactly what it is made of.

Astronomers have identified meteorites – chunks of rock from space that have fallen to Earth – as leftover pieces of the ring of material that circled the Sun and from which the planets formed. These pieces of rock are particularly rich in four elements – iron, oxygen, magnesium and silicon – as well as an alloy of iron and nickel. If the Earth were made of the same mixture of material, in the same proportions, it would have exactly the measured overall density of our planet, which is 5,520 kilograms per cubic metre, or 0.2 pounds per cubic inch. But if you took away the iron and nickel from a meteoritic mixture the size of the Earth, you would be left with a volume that is the same as the Earth's mantle, and a chemical composition that is almost identical to the material actually found there. And the amount of iron 'missing' from the mixture is exactly the amount needed to make the core of the Earth. This very simple calculation tells us that the core of the Earth must be mostly made of iron, with some nickel too. Our planet is made from the same stuff as meteorites, but the iron and nickel has settled to the middle, leaving lighter material behind.

Knowing the composition of the Earth's core allows you to work out its temperature, because the inner core is solid while the outer core is liquid. So the boundary between the inner core and the outer core must be at the melting point of an iron-nickel mixture at the pressure corresponding to a depth of 5,100 kilometres (3,100 miles) below the surface of the Earth, where iron is squeezed to a density twelve times the density of water. Laboratory experiments show that this temperature is roughly 5,000° C (9,000° F), which, as it happens, and entirely by coincidence, is very nearly the same as the temperature at the surface of the Sun. Because a solid lump of iron and nickel is a very good conductor of heat, we can be sure that this is pretty much the temperature across the entire inner core. So the temperature at the centre of the Earth is also about 5,000° C.

The structure of the iron-nickel core, with a solid inner core surrounded by a liquid outer core, is responsible for one of the most striking features of the planet – its magnetic field, which among other things shields us from harmful cosmic radiation. Nobody knows exactly how the magnetic field is generated, but it must be a result of physical currents of material, circulating in the electrically conducting outer core and generating magnetism as they do so, like a dynamo. Both calculations and experiments show that this kind of thing will not work with a completely liquid core, where fluid would circulate more evenly. The best explanation for the Earth's magnetic field is that the solid core is surrounded by cylinders of swirling material in the outer core, like a tennis ball surrounded by a ring of fat marker pens standing on their ends. A combination of convection and the twisting forces caused by the Earth's rotation (the Coriolis effect) generates a magnetic field in each 'marker pen' that contributes to the overall magnetic field. But in 4 billion years' time, when the entire core has solidified, the Earth will lose its powerful magnetic field. Bad news for any life forms around then, but not something for us to worry about.

That's as much as we know about the deep interior of the Earth; the next question, though, brings us back to the surface, and the relationship between the planet and ourselves.

Why Does Blood Taste Salty Like the Sea?

The question I was actually asked was: 'Why does the sea taste like blood?' But this is putting the cart before the horse, because the sea came first and blood evolved later. So in order to find the answer, I have to turn it round, and start by asking: 'Why is the sea salty?' Keep the blood question in the back of your mind for now.

Oceans dominate the surface of the Earth. Most of our planet is covered by a thin layer of water – salty water, making up 97 per cent of all the water on the surface of the planet. These oceans provide the home of most of life on Earth, and they carry about 50 million billion tonnes of dissolved salt – mostly common salt, sodium chloride. The oceans are about 3.5 per cent sodium and chlorine, in terms of weight, so each litre of sea water contains about 35 grams of salt. There are other salts in sea water, notably potassium and calcium, but sodium and chlorine together make up about 85 per cent of the 'solids' in the oceans. If all this salt could be extracted and spread out evenly over the land surface, it would make a layer more than 160 metres thick.

But the oceans are tiny compared with the layers of rock discussed in the previous answer. The bottom of the deepest ocean is only about eleven kilometres below the surface of the sea, and if we generously say that the abode of life extends to the top of the tallest mountain, some nine kilometres above sea level, the entire life zone of the Earth is confined to a layer no more than twenty kilometres thick. In proportion to the diameter of the Earth, this is equivalent to the thickness of the skin of an apple relative to the size of the apple. So the composition of the oceans is profoundly affected by the geological processes involved in plate tectonics and sea-floor spreading, especially the volcanic activity at mid-ocean ridges. But none of this was known about in 1715, when Edmond Halley came up with the first scientific explanation for the saltiness of the sea.

Halley made the reasonable guess, for the time he lived in, that rivers pick up impurities from the rocks they travel over and deposit them in the sea, where the concentration of salts build up. They build up because the fresh water evaporates, leaving the salts behind, and the water is carried back over the land as vapour, where it rains and completes the cycle. He suggested that this could be used to estimate the age of the Earth, by measuring how much salt there is in rivers and working out how long it would take for the sea to build up its present saltiness. But he couldn't apply the idea because he didn't have measurements of the amount of salt being carried by all the rivers of the world – the concentration of salt in the sea is actually about 200 times the concentration found in rivers – or the volume of the oceans.

It's probably just as well Halley couldn't do the calculation because it wouldn't have worked. To start with, it is based on the assumption that the oceans started out as pure fresh water, and there is no evidence for this (there is no evidence against it, either, but that isn't much help). Then, it assumes that the ocean is like an enclosed inland lake, always the same size, and that all the salt dumped in it stays there. We now know that the oceans are always changing on geological timescales, with the sea bed sometimes being raised up by tectonic activity and drying out to form great salt beds, while in other places the sea floor is pushed under a continent, melting and creating volcanic activity that spews a chemical brew into the atmosphere, and lays down new rocks that incorporate many of the minerals from the sea, providing the raw materials for future weathering by rain and rivers that return those minerals back to the sea. It is estimated by geophysicists that this activity is roughly in a state of equilibrium today, so that the saltiness of the seas stays roughly the same. But that wasn't always the case.

To work out how the saltiness of the sea has changed over geological time we first need to know where all the water came from in the first place, and that is still something the experts argue about. They agree, as I have explained, that the Earth formed about 4.5 billion years ago, from the accumulation of debris in the young Solar System, with rocks crashing into each other and building up a proto-planet that tugged more debris onto itself by gravity, sweeping its surroundings clear. The impact of those rocky meteorites heated the young planet into a molten ball, which gradually cooled, over a few hundred million years, and formed a solid crust. One school of thought says that gases from the interior, pouring out from volcanoes, formed the atmosphere around the Earth and provided the water vapour that fell as rain to make the first oceans. The rival school of thought, which seems more plausible to me, suggests that icy debris from further out from the Sun, left over from the formation of the planets and essentially the same as comets, carried water down onto the young planet in the final stages of its development. But either way, there is geological evidence that the early ocean was established a bit less than 4 billion years ago, when the Earth was still much more active, geologically speaking, than it is today. And it is quite possible, of course, that both processes were involved in making that ocean.

However it formed, the early ocean must have been enriched with minerals, including the salt we are interested in, by the violent underwater geological activity of the young Earth. The geological evidence tells us that the ocean ridges were more extensive and more active then, as you would expect when the planet was still cooling from its primordial state, and that the first pieces of continental crust were smaller than the continents today and scattered around the globe. Continental crust has grown over geological time because of volcanic activity, especially along the margins where the sea floor is being pushed under continental crust. The best way geologists can estimate just how much salt there was in the early ocean is to add up the amount of salt in great beds around the globe and calculate the effect this would have on salinity if it were all dissolved back into the sea.

These salt beds are huge; the amount of salt they contain is measured in thousands of billions of tonnes. Enormous deposits are found in many places, including Australia, Canada, Iran, Oman, Pakistan, Peru and Saudi Arabia. They were laid down during rare phases of tectonic activity when supercontinents like Pangea were breaking up and creating extensive shallow seas (a bit like the present-day Mediterranean Sea and Black Sea), which then became landlocked and dried out, after which the salt was buried in further phases of tectonic activity. This happened more than once during the history of the Earth, but the breakup of Pangea's predecessor, Rodinia (sometimes known as Pangea I), at the end of the interval of geological time called the Precambrian, about 540 million years ago, is especially interesting for life forms like us.

The Precambrian gets its name because it comes before the Cambrian, and the Cambrian is when life diversified and spread across the Earth. Although the Precambrian covers 90 per cent of the history of the Earth, life in the Precambrian ocean was restricted to simple organisms, such as the bacteria known as blue-green algae. One of the reasons for this was the high salinity of the oceans. At the beginning of the Cambrian, there was a reduction in salinity, which, among other chemical changes that proved advantageous to life, made it easier for oxygen to be dissolved in sea water. These chemical changes encouraged the explosion of life that spread out of the oceans and across the land. And that explosion of life, visible in the fossil record, is why geologists label this as the beginning of the Cambrian.*

So the explosion of life on Earth was closely linked to a dramatic decline in the salinity of the oceans. Just how much the salinity fell at that time is still a subject of geological debate. But it may be that part of the answer comes not from geology but from biology. Which ties in with the blood part of the question I was asked.

For most of the history of life on Earth, that life consisted of single-celled organisms floating in the sea. I described how cells work in my book *Eight Improbable Possibilities*, but all that matters here is that what goes on inside cells depends on the chemistry of DNA and the way it interacts with other molecules to operate the workings of the cell. All this is surrounded by a cell wall that allows some things (what we might loosely call nutrients) in from

---

* The name Cambrian, like other geological terms, can simply be regarded as a label. It actually comes from a variation on the name of Wales (Cymru), which is where pioneering geologists found some interesting rocks of the appropriate age.

Badwater Salt Flats, California, United States
Mikenorton, CC BY-SA 4.0, via Wikimedia Commons

outside and lets other things (waste products) out. The outside, of course, was originally the salty sea. Blood is like a sea in miniature. It consists of a watery liquid, called plasma, in which different kinds of cells, including the red cells that give it its colour, float. This watery portion of blood has a concentration of salt and other substances that is remarkably similar to sea water. About 55 per cent of blood is plasma, so cells make up less than half of the total. Blood cells float in their own private ocean.

The first person to draw attention to the evolutionary implications of this was the Canadian biochemist Archibald Macallum, in a scientific paper published in 1926. He realised that this similarity implies that our ancestors evolved in the sea, and our blood carries a memory of the conditions in which they evolved. You might wonder why it took so long for someone to point out what probably seems obvious to you, but Charles Darwin's book *On the Origin of Species* had only been published in 1859, a year after Macallum was born. The interval from 1859 to 1926 was only 57 years, little more than half the interval from 1926 to when I am writing these words, and the full implications of evolutionary theory had yet to sink in.

Ten years later, Arthur Pearse, then professor of zoology at Duke University, published a book entitled *The Migrations of Animals from Sea to Land* in which he said, 'the general similarity of the bloods of animals to seawater has been interpreted as indicating that all animals originated in the sea' and referred to the 'common belief' that blood is a modified form of sea water. And in her bestseller *The Sea Around Us*, published in 1951, the pioneering environmentalist Rachel Carson wrote: 'Fish, amphibian, and reptile, warm-blooded bird and mammal – each of us carries in our veins a salty stream in which the elements sodium, potassium, and calcium are combined in almost the same proportions as in sea water.'

In 1957, the First International Symposium of the Origin of Life on the Earth was held in Moscow. The Russian evolutionary biologist Raisa Berg used the occasion to spell out to this specialist audience that 'the most important arguments in favour of the hypothesis that life originated exclusively in the ocean' are, first, 'the similarity between the salt composition of the body fluids of land animals and that of the waters of the ocean', and second, that the 'similarity in the salt composition of the waters of the ocean and that of the body fluids of land animals' could only be accounted for by evolution.

The point is that the first organisms that closed themselves off from the sea still needed an internal liquid to carry stuff around their bodies, bringing nutrients to cells and carrying waste products away, and this stuff was essentially sea water modified from the water that surrounded them at the moment in geological time when this revolutionary step took place. Ever since, while the salinity of the oceans changed, the chemical processes going on inside the evolving animals maintained their blood at the same concentration as before.

So just how similar is blood (or rather, plasma) to sea water, and what does that tell us about evolution? Remember that on average, sea water in the world's oceans has a salinity of about 3.5 per cent. The salinity of human blood is 0.9 per cent, so sea water is roughly 3.5 times as salty as blood. And not just human blood. All vertebrate animals (animals with backbones, which means all fish, birds, mammals, amphibians and reptiles*) have the same unique salt content of their blood. This is one of many pieces of evidence that show they are all descended from a common ancestor.

Putting it the other way round, vertebrate blood, not just your blood, is only about a quarter as salty as sea water. At first sight, although this is close enough to convince us that blood is modified sea water (after all, blood might have been a hundred times saltier, or one-hundredth as salty, if there were no connection) this looks like an intriguing problem for evolutionary biologists to solve. If sea water has been getting less salty as geological time passes, how can our blood 'remember' a saltiness less than that of today? There is, though, an obvious way to explain this. Fossil and other evidence shows that the

....

* Presumably the same applies to now-extinct vertebrate species such as the dinosaurs; in all probability your blood is pretty much the same as dinosaur blood.

first vertebrates evolved about 500 million years ago, and if the evolutionary biologists are right, they did so in water only about a quarter as salty as the seas are, on average, today. The clue lies in those words 'on average'.

One of the things I still have trouble getting my head round, although I know logically that it must be so, is that when we say all vertebrates are descended from a common ancestor, we mean literally that. One single individual in which the genetic changes (mutations in DNA) that began the steps along a path leading to the development of backbones occurred. This individual must have had relations, of course. Members of what was then the same species, with which it could breed. But only the descendants of that individual evolved along the different lines that led to all fish, birds, mammals, amphibians and reptiles. And that one unique individual need not have lived in the depths of the ocean. The biochemical evidence tells us that it lived in a relatively dilute part of the ocean, such as a shallow estuary where fresh water from rivers mixed with the salt water of the sea. There are even good reasons why such an environment would have been good for life 500 million years ago. The shallow waters would let the sunlight penetrate, providing the energy on which all life on the surface of the Earth depends. And the reduced saltiness of these waters would have allowed more oxygen to dissolve in it, encouraging life to proliferate and therefore encouraging evolution.

So there is the answer to the question 'why is blood salty?' Because about 500 million years ago the ancestor of all vertebrates was living in a warm, shallow estuary in water with salinity of about 0.9 per cent, that is, with about nine grams of salt dissolved in each litre of water. But before I move on to look at another intriguing evolutionary question, it's worth expanding on this a little by looking at how one line of vertebrate evolution, the fishes, have coped with living in water with different salinities.

Fish are particularly interesting because for land animals the situation, as far as maintaining the saltiness of their blood was concerned, is more boring; it stayed the same once they were out of the water. Mammals like us, birds and reptiles take in salts and fresh water in their food and drink, use what they need to maintain the concentration in the blood they are used to (which means what they had evolved to use before they left the sea) and excrete enough to maintain the same balance – not just the same in an individual animal over its lifetime, but in all the generations since our ancestors left the sea. The outside world doesn't have much effect on this, as long as there is food to eat and water to drink.

But fish have different problems to contend with. Like us, they have to take in the water they need from their surroundings, before processing it into the saltiness required for their blood. But the saltiness of the water they take in depends on where they live. And in spite of this, fish blood – all vertebrate fish blood – has the same saltiness as our blood.

Fish that live in brackish water, such as the shallow estuaries where it seems likely that vertebrates first appeared, have little problem with this, because the saltiness of the water around them isn't much different from the saltiness of their blood. But fish that live out in the open ocean are surrounded by water significantly more salty than the concentration they need for their blood. As their ancestors moved into this environment, over many generations, they evolved a biochemical mechanism to deal with this. They are forced to drink water containing much more salt than they need, but they filter this out in their kidneys and excrete small amounts of highly concentrated urine that gets rid of the excess. They also use a mechanism to pump sodium out of their gills, again using energy.

Fish whose ancestors went the other way, from brackish water into fresh water, evolved exactly the opposite mechanism. They need pretty much all the salt they can get from their food to maintain the concentration in their blood, and they hold onto it, excreting large amounts of very dilute urine (up to a third of their body weight each day) – and, you guessed it, they have a mechanism in their gills to absorb more salts.

By and large, this means that fish from the ocean cannot live in fresh water, and fish from fresh-water lakes and rivers cannot live in the sea. But as so often with rules, it is the exceptions to this rule that are most interesting. Fish such as salmon and eels spend part of their lives in fresh water and part of their lives in the sea. Their DNA carries the biochemical code for each kind of behaviour, and there is a biological switch that flips the biochemistry of the individual from one pattern to another at the appropriate time. And where does the switch take place? These fishes that have to switch their salt balance mechanism from one system to another typically make the change in a brackish estuary on the way between the salt water and freshwater habitats, where the saltiness of the water matches the saltiness of their blood.

All this highlights a key feature of evolution. It has to build on what has gone before. If you were designing a fish for, say, a salty ocean, it would be simpler to give it blood matching the saltiness of the water. The biochemical processes that adjust the saltiness of the blood to a lower level are more complicated, use chemical resources and require more energy, all of which makes them a handicap compared with an intelligently designed fish. But evolution cannot throw out the mechanism that worked in brackish water and start again; it has to build on what it has got. Similarly, in many species alive today, there are often reminders of the way their ancestors lived, features that are no longer important but haven't been got rid of. Even our own bodies have some obvious evolutionary leftovers of this kind, as the next answer illustrates.

QUESTION

Why Are Men Bigger than Women?

Of course, not all men are bigger than all women. But among many different human populations, in different parts of the world, the average height of a man is greater than the average height of a woman. There must be some reason for this, and the way to find the explanation is to follow up Charles Darwin's advice, that we should proceed by 'looking at Man, as a Naturalist would at any other mammiferous animal'.* By 'Man', of course, Darwin meant the human species, and his point is that evolution has operated on our species in the same way that it operates on all species. For the benefit of any doubters, he offers a couple of rhetorical questions:

> He who wishes to decide whether man is the modified descendant of some pre-existing form, would probably first enquire whether man varies, however slightly, in bodily structure and in mental faculties;

* See *The Descent of Man*: http://darwin-online.org.uk/

and if so, whether the variations are transmitted to his offspring in accordance with the laws which prevail with the lower animals. Again, are the variations the result, as far as our ignorance permits us to judge, of the same general causes, and are they governed by the same general laws, as in the case of other organisms?

The answer to all this is, of course, 'yes'. As in other organisms, human offspring differ slightly from their parents, producing a variety of individuals. Over millions of years, if individuals have characteristics that make them more successful, in the sense of leaving more offspring in their turn, then those characteristics will spread among the population and become common. That is what is meant by natural selection. This is a slow process. The few thousand years that have elapsed since humans developed civilisation are not enough to have had a significant influence on it, and we all have characteristics that have evolved in this way and were successful for our ancestors. So men being larger than women must have been a successful evolutionary 'strategy' for our ancestors, even if it is not so important in modern society.

This is actually rather odd. It seems normal to most people, because few of us are familiar with the private lives of other species. But in other species, it is much more common for the female to be bigger than the male.

This has obvious evolutionary advantages. The female has to devote a lot of resources to making eggs, and in the case of mammals, nurturing the developing embryo inside her own body. The male seems to serve no role* except to fertilise the eggs then run (or fly, or swim) off to fertilise some other female's eggs (or in a few cases, to be eaten by the female to provide more resources for the developing eggs). This rule of females being bigger than males applies overwhelmingly in the insect world, and since there are vastly more insect species than all other animal species put together, this means it applies for most species across the animal kingdom as a whole. It is less general in the world of mammiferous animals, but even here, females are the larger sex in, among others, rabbits, bats and common seals. It is so easy to see the evolutionary advantage of females being bigger than males that the way to get a handle on why men are bigger than women is to look at the other exceptions to this rule and try to find out what they have in common.

Although we cannot be sure exactly how sexual reproduction got started, as I have already hinted, it leads to different evolutionary strategies for males and females, leading to a competition between the sexes that is part

* I nearly said, 'serves no purpose', but, of course, evolution does not have a purpose, it operates blindly.

of the evolutionary competition between individuals in any species.

This is worth spelling out, since it is easy to be confused about exactly which individuals are involved in the competition that is a key part of evolution by natural selection. The classic example involves lions who hunt deer for their food. At first sight, you might think that the lion, after food, is competing with the deer, trying to escape. But the story is a little more subtle than that. The lion will catch the slowest deer, so what really matters for the deer is not running faster than a lion, but to be faster than the slowest runner in the herd. The deer are competing with each other to not be slow. In successive generations, the fastest deer survive, and because they live to pass on their DNA, the overall population of deer get faster as the generations succeed one another. Similarly, the lions that are better adapted to catching and eating deer, with speed, sharp claws and good teeth, will do best at bringing home a meal for the pride, providing food for her offspring and thereby ensuring the survival of her own DNA.

This is another interesting point. It is indeed the female lion that does the hunting and brings home the food. The male, though, is significantly bigger, even though he lazes around most of the time. How does this help to ensure that his DNA gets passed on? Who is he competing with? He is competing with other males, who would like to move in and take over his harem of females.

Which provides us with our first hint of why men are bigger than women; but before I go into that further, I ought to spell out a bit more about how evolution works.

There are two extreme strategies that offer a good chance of getting copies of an individual's DNA passed on to successive generations. The first is to throw out a huge number of copies of your genetic material in the hope that a few will survive. This is called the 'elm-oyster model' because it is practised by both those species. If you look at the proliferation of seedlings that grow under the canopy of an elm tree, you can see this strategy at work; few of us have actually seen oyster larvae, but they are tiny and produced in a similar profusion. The profligacy of the strategy is highlighted when you stop to remind yourself that the population of elm trees in a forest will stay the same if just one of the many seedlings each tree produces in its entire lifetime survives to grow into a mature tree. Here is competition with a vengeance, plenty of opportunity for evolution by natural selection to work. Once again, the competition is between members of the same species, and the ones that are best fitted to their environment (best fitted, in the sense of a piece fitting into a jigsaw puzzle) are selected by nature to survive and reproduce in their turn.

At the other extreme, there is the strategy I like to call 'all your eggs in one basket', because it is literally the approach used by nesting birds. In this strategy, very few offspring are produced at any one time, but they are carefully protected and nurtured until they are able to look after themselves. We can see this very clearly in the behaviour of many birds, and the most striking thing is that in most cases it is so much effort that both parents are needed to ensure the survival of the chicks. In the elm-oyster model, the parent does nothing at all to help the offspring; but with all the eggs in one basket, two parents work, in many cases to the point of exhaustion, to raise the brood. We are all so familiar with the life cycle of birds that it is hardly necessary to labour the point. But there is one interesting consequence that may be relevant to our own (human) story. Where the parents share the work in this way, there is often very little outward difference between the male and female parents. Swans are the classic example – they lay only a few eggs each year, one at a time, both parents share the parental duties and although the male is slightly bigger than the female, at a quick glance it is hard to tell them apart.

Of course, there are other bird species where the differences between the sexes are obvious. A peacock, for example, with its large and colourful tail, could never be mistaken for a peahen. But these differences are often a result of the competition between males to attract a mate. It is clear that peahens are indeed attracted to peacocks with big colourful tails, and although nobody knows how this started, clearly, if females prefer bigger tails then males with bigger tails pass on their DNA to future generations, and tails get bigger and bigger until they become such a hindrance that the males cannot survive. But this kind of sexual selection is another story.

In overall terms, the eggs in one basket strategy is ultimately no different from the elm-oyster model. It is still true that if each pair of, say, swans produce in their entire lifetime a single pair of offspring that survive to adulthood the population stays the same. There is still an enormous 'wastage' of individuals, and a few well-adapted survivors. Something to ponder next time you see a mother duck being followed across a pond by a string of ducklings. Chances are, none of them will survive.

But these extreme examples of reproductive strategies are not the whole story. There are many species that operate mixed strategies of various kinds, with some parental care but much less than that provided by a pair of swans. There is a balance to be struck between having lots of offspring, so there are many copies of your DNA 'out there', and being able to look after the offspring long enough for them to have a chance of survival and, crucially, reproducing in turn. This feeds directly into our understanding of why in some mammiferous species males are bigger than females, while in others females are bigger than males.

Mammals are particularly intriguing because the appropriate male and female strategies for evolutionary success are essentially the two extreme examples I have just described. The female has no choice but to produce a relatively small number of offspring and to nurture them for a greater or lesser time. The male could, in principle, impregnate large numbers of females and not bother about what happens to the offspring. The snag for the male, however, is that if he does not contribute to the nurturing, the offspring may not survive. Human biology provides an extreme example of this distinction, because newborn humans are so helpless for so long (why that is so is another interesting evolutionary story, linked to our large brain size, but beyond the scope of this answer). A woman could at most become pregnant about once a year, and even allowing for a few sets of twins or triplets, it would be remarkable if any human female produced more than 50 children in her lifetime. But a man could, if he could find enough willing partners, easily impregnate a different woman each week, and produce 50 children in a single year – then 50 more the following year, and so on for decades. The problem is providing for those children if they are to survive long enough for his DNA to be passed on to any further generations.

That this is indeed a feasible proposition is confirmed by the documented records of human harems. In the most extreme example for which reliable records have survived, the last Sharifian Emperor of Morocco, Moulay Ismail, had fathered a total of 525 sons and 342 daughters by 1703, and didn't stop there (he died in 1727 at the age of 55), although the later records are not complete. Great for him, but remember this is also a good deal for the women, since it ensured that their DNA was passed on to future generations. The relevant point is that he was a rich and powerful man (his nickname 'The Bloodthirsty' gives you an idea of his power) who had the resources to maintain a large number of wives and all those children. The ordinary men of his time, and all ordinary men in prehistoric times, could not have achieved anything like this.

A non-human example helps to make the point that just as deer are competing with one another to see who can run fast enough, males are competing with one another to obtain mates and produce offspring. The example comes from a study carried out by the splendidly named Burney LeBoeuf and his colleagues from the Santa Cruz campus of the University of California, and it involves a colony of elephant seals that they monitored for several years.

The results of the observations from just one season at the colony on Año Nuevo Island are sufficient here. In that season, there were 115 males in the colony, but a few of them each jealously guarded a large harem of females, while most of the males were pushed out to the fringes and tried to achieve a mating, while the 'owner' of a harem was otherwise engaged. This was seldom successful. Altogether just five of the 115 males accounted for 123 out of 144 matings – just over 85 per cent of the

Moulay Ismail
18th-century engraver, anonymous, public domain, via Wikimedia Commons

total. In order to achieve this success, the males have to be much bigger than the females, not to overpower them but to fight off other males. The biggest males have the biggest harems.

But even the modest success of the few males who did sneak in behind a harem-owner's back highlights another relevant point. It concerns what is called paternity certainty, and it rests upon the crucial difference between the sexes. In mammals, the mother has no doubt that her offspring are indeed her own. Even a bird cannot be quite sure that all of the eggs in a nest are hers, as the example of the cuckoo demonstrates. But a woman who gives birth to a baby and suckles it can have no uncertainty about where it came from, even if, as is sometimes the case, she does not know who the father is. The male has no such certainty. The only way he can be absolutely certain that the offspring produced by a female he has mated with are indeed his is if he has kept all other males away from her – as the elephant seals try, not with 100 per cent success, to do.

In evolutionary terms, even in a species where two parents are needed to raise the offspring successfully, the female might not 'mind' who she mates with as long as there is some male around to help with the child-rearing. Equally, a male who manages to sneak a mating with a female that is being protected by another male can get many of the benefits with few of the costs. This provides a limit on how big a harem like that of the elephant seal can be; if there are too many females for one male to guard, he ends up with all of the costs for few of the benefits. All this has intriguing implications for human behaviour, which I won't go into here, but you can ponder for yourself; for now, I will stick to the fundamental fact that a male can only be certain of paternity if he keeps other males away.

This strategy, however, can also pose problems, at least in non-mammiferous species. An entertaining example (entertaining for us, not for them) comes from the behaviour of starlings. The strategy they have evolved is for the male to stay with the female to ensure that no other male can mate with her. This means that after a clutch of eggs has been laid in the nest, the male goes away with the female when she is looking for food. Sometimes, another female will visit the unguarded nest and leave one of her own eggs in it. The extra egg looks the same as all the others, and the pair the nest belongs to look after it, and the resulting hatchling, without being aware that they have a stranger in their midst. The evolutionary biologists who study such things infer that as far as the males are concerned, the extra cost of raising one additional chick is not as great as the potential cost of ending up with a whole nest full of eggs that they have not fathered.

But this is getting away from the point under discussion. I have now gathered enough evidence to be able to answer the question 'why are men bigger than women?' from the point of view of an alien visiting Earth and studying the behaviour of different kinds of mammiferous animals. Such an unbiased observer would notice that males are bigger than females in many species, and careful measurements would reveal that the degree of this sexual dimorphism is directly related to the number of mates that are, for want of a better word, protected by the male. I have already mentioned lions and elephant seals. In a species more closely related to ourselves, the alien biologist would note that a whole troop of gorillas will be dominated by a single male who is roughly 30 per cent taller and twice as heavy as the females; he keeps all other adult males at bay (until he becomes old and feeble) and has no uncertainty about the paternity of all the young in the troop. Although humans share about 98 per cent of their DNA with the gorilla, the average difference in height between men and women, taking the population of the planet as a whole, is only about 8 per cent. Our unbiased alien biologist, 'looking at Man, as a Naturalist would at any other mammiferous animal', would conclude that in pre-civilisation times, each successful male would have been able to keep a 'harem' of two or at most three females, while the unsuccessful men had to resort to the same sort of tactics as the unsuccessful male elephant seals, trying to sneak a mating on the sly.

All of this makes sense if you think about conditions in prehistoric times, from the evolutionary point of view of both men and women. A family group of one man and two women would be an effective number for child-rearing, especially for assistance with birth and its immediate aftermath, while one man would hardly be able to protect, or guard, more than three women and the various children in the family, even if all the adults were involved in things like food gathering. The fact that this was a successful evolutionary strategy is all around us. The mammal world is dominated by people, not by lions, or gorillas, or elephant seals. But one result of this success is that the difference in size between men and women is no longer relevant to evolution; we know why men have evolved to be bigger than women, but this dimorphism has outlived its usefulness and is just a memory of the way of life of our ancient ancestors.

QUESTION

10

Why Is the Sky Blue?

If you have already read the answer to Question 1, you know why the sky is dark at night. But if you have been thinking about that answer, you may have begun to wonder why the sky is not also dark in the daytime, except in the direction of the Sun. After all, the arguments I used to explain the darkness of the night sky apply with equal force in the daytime. And pictures taken by astronauts on the Moon show that the sky is indeed dark there all the time, except in the direction of the Sun. The answer must have something to do with the presence of an atmosphere around the Earth but not around the Moon. But I don't intend to fob you off just by saying that the answer is 'because the Earth has an atmosphere'. The question becomes: How does the atmosphere make the sky blue?

As with so much in science, the explanation starts with an investigation carried out by Isaac Newton, back in the 17th century. In the middle of the 1660s, Newton had just obtained his bachelor's degree from Cambridge and had returned home to Woolsthorpe, in Lincolnshire, to avoid an outbreak of the plague. This resulted in what is known as his '*annus mirabilis*', the 'miracle year' in which, free from any outside distractions, he made several important scientific discoveries. The one that is relevant here came from his investigation of light.

It was well known by Newton's time that when light from the Sun passes through a triangular piece of glass, called a prism, it emerges from the other side in a pattern of colours, like the colours of the rainbow. Newton became intrigued by the phenomenon after he bought such a piece of glass being sold as a curiosity at a fair. The light is also bent (refracted) on its way through the glass, and the different colours emerge at slightly different angles. Before Newton came along, the obvious explanation seemed to be that the 'pure' white light was picking up colours (impurities) from the glass on its way through the prism. But Newton devised an ingenious experiment to test this idea.

He worked in a room kept dark by heavy blinds on the window, with one small hole to allow a beam of sunlight into the room.* When the beam was intercepted by a prism held at the correct angle, the light emerging from the other side produced a spectrum of colours on the wall opposite the window – exactly the same colours

....
* You can still visit the room, and the rest of the house, at his family home in Woolsthorpe.

as in a rainbow, in exactly the same order. It was Newton who recorded them as red, orange, yellow, green, blue, indigo and violet. There are, though, no sharp boundaries between the colours: red blends into orange, orange into yellow, and so on. But now came his critical test. If the old ideas about light were correct, putting a second prism in the beam of coloured light ought to produce an even more colourful spectrum. But Newton found that if he put the second prism upside down relative to the first one, like this ($\Delta \nabla$), the rays of coloured light were recombined back into a single beam of 'pure' white light. In a further experiment, Newton arranged for one single coloured ray of light to pass through a second prism. It emerged on the other side unchanged.

There was only one conclusion that could explain all this. Instead of white light being pure, it is actually a mixture of all the colours of the rainbow, and each of those colours is itself a pure form of light. As a bonus, this also explains how rainbows themselves are produced by refraction, although that process also involves reflection inside water droplets, which is why the Sun has to be behind you for you to see a rainbow.

The details of what is going on had to wait for a better understanding of light, which began to emerge in the early 19th century, when Thomas Young in England and Augustin-Jean Fresnel in France independently showed that light travels as a form of wave, and measurements revealed that red light has the longest wavelengths in the visible spectrum (with a wavelength of about 750 nanometres), while violet has the shortest (with a wavelength of about 380 nm).* Blue light has a wavelength of about 450 nm. To put this in perspective, a human hair is about 50,000 nm thick. What kind of waves they were remained a mystery until the 1860s, when James Clerk Maxwell, building on the work of Michael Faraday, came up with a set of equations describing how electromagnetic waves move through space and found that these waves travel at the speed of light. This evidence that light travels as a form of electromagnetic wave emerged at exactly the same time that the Irish polymath John Tyndall found the basic phenomenon that explains why the sky is blue. But his work was a spin-off from a study that now has far greater importance – his investigation of what we now call the greenhouse effect.

At the beginning of the 19th century, the astronomer William Herschel had been investigating the spectrum of sunlight when he discovered that there is a 'colour' of radiation with wavelength longer than red light, which our eyes cannot see, but which warms the surface it touches. This became known as infrared radiation. The warmth you can feel if you hold your hand near, but not touching, a radiator is produced by infrared radiation. There is

---

* A nanometre is one-billionth of a metre.

also radiation with wavelengths shorter than violet light, called ultraviolet radiation. Several scientists, most notably the Frenchman Joseph Fourier, had speculated that the atmosphere of the Earth somehow acts like a blanket, keeping the surface of our planet warmer than it would be without an atmosphere, but it was Tyndall who carried out experiments that confirmed this by measuring the amount of infrared radiation captured by different gases. The experiments involved passing radiation from a hot source through a long glass tube and measuring how much heat got through the gas in the tube. He found that nitrogen and oxygen, the main components of the atmosphere, absorb very little infrared, but carbon dioxide and water vapour absorb a lot. The conclusion is that energy from the Sun in the visible part of the spectrum warms the surface of the Earth, then the warm surface radiates energy back outwards in the form of infrared radiation, which is trapped in the atmosphere. As Tyndall put it in a presentation to the Royal Society in June 1859: 'When the heat is absorbed by the planet, it is so changed in quality that the rays emanating from the planet cannot get with the same freedom back into space. Thus the atmosphere admits of the entrance of the solar heat; but checks its exit, and the result is a tendency to accumulate heat at the surface of the planet.' Without these gases, Tyndall wrote, the Earth would be 'held fast in the iron grip of frost'.

The accuracy of that comment can be seen by comparing the temperature on Earth with that of the airless Moon. Averaging over the entire surface, both day and night, the mean temperature of the Moon is −18° C; the equivalent average temperature of the Earth is 15° C. That 33-degree difference is almost entirely due to the natural greenhouse effect,* although a little heat does leak out from the interior of the Earth. These experiments continued, alongside other work, into the 1860s, and a variation on the theme provided a key insight into why the sky is blue.

The reason for the blueness of the sky puzzled many scientists at the time, and Tyndall was particularly interested because he was a keen mountaineer and had often observed clear blue skies in the Alps, a bluish tint in light reflected from snow, and the way light is scattered in clouds and fog. The big discovery he made came thanks to improvements in electric lights in the 1860s. In 1868, Tyndall was experimenting with artificial clouds in his carbon dioxide tube when he noticed that if the tube contained dusty gas and a beam of white electric light was shone along it, from the side 'the track of the beam is distinctly blue'. In further experiments, he showed that the blue colour could be produced as clouds formed in the

* And the difference is now increasing as gases released by human activities are enhancing the effect.

John Tyndall
Smithsonian Institution via Wikimedia Commons

tube, that it was stronger for smaller particles, and that it got more feeble as the size of the particles increased. The effect only worked for very small particles – 'a very small fraction of the length of a wave of violet light', as Tyndall put it in a paper read out at the Royal Society in January 1869. But he could not tell exactly which particles were involved, nor explain why blue light should be singled out in this way. The next step was taken by John William Strutt (better known as Lord Rayleigh, a title he inherited in 1873 on the death of his father).

Following from Tyndall's work, Rayleigh published several papers on light scattering, culminating in a contribution that appeared in 1881. With the insight provided by Maxwell, he was able to put numbers into the calculation of the way light interacts with electrically charged particles, although at that time, almost twenty years before the discovery of the electron, nobody knew exactly what the charged particles involved were. The key fact that emerged from Rayleigh's work is that for particles much smaller than the wavelength of the radiation involved, the amount of scattering produced in this way is proportional to 1 divided by the fourth power of the wavelength of the electromagnetic radiation. In other words, the shorter the wavelength is, the more scattering there is. For obvious reasons, this is called an inverse power law. From the wavelengths I have given you for red and blue light, it is simple to calculate that the blue light is scattered about eight times as much as red light by the particles – atoms and molecules, we now know – in the air. This process is known as Rayleigh scattering, which seems a bit unfair on Tyndall, who discovered the phenomenon, but so it goes.

This is actually all you need to understand why the sky is blue, but there is a piece of icing on the cake that I cannot resist mentioning involving Albert Einstein. In 1910, as part of a larger study of scattering processes, Einstein was able to refine these calculations and among other things use them to estimate the sizes of the particles (molecules) involved – much smaller than the wavelengths of visible light.* The details do not affect the main story, but his involvement gives me the opportunity to point out that our understanding of why the sky is blue begins with Isaac Newton and ends with Albert Einstein, the two greatest physicists who ever lived. Which highlights how simple questions can require big answers.

Armed with all this information, I can now explain why the sky is blue. It is because the blue light from the Sun doesn't simply get bounced around from one molecule to another, like the ball in a pinball machine bouncing from one bumper to another. What actually happens is that a molecule absorbs the light, gaining energy in the

---

* Strictly speaking, the process involves electrons bound to molecules by electric forces.

process, and then almost immediately radiates it away again in all directions, losing the energy it has just gained. The colour that is radiated is the same as the colour that was absorbed, but the whole process happens eight times more efficiently for blue light than for red light. This happens repeatedly, spreading the blue light from molecule to molecule around the whole sky, with some of it ending up going down towards the Earth (and our eyes), and some heading upward, out towards space. All of the blue light from the sky, whichever part of the sky you look at, is sunlight that has been scattered in this way.

The red light is not scattered so easily by this process, but it does bounce off dust particles and water droplets in the air, much more like the way the balls in a pinball machine bounce off the buffers. So it can be reflected off clouds and dust in the air, and this kind of scattering is most effective at sunrise and sunset, when the Sun is low on the horizon and light has a long way to travel through the atmosphere, making the sky low on the horizon red at sunsets and sunrises.

All well and good. But I hope you have noticed that this raises another question. If Rayleigh scattering obeys the inverse power law I have just described (which it does), why isn't the sky violet (or maybe purple, allowing for the blue as well)? The answer to this supplementary question involves both physics and biology. The physics has to do with the nature of sunlight. The Sun radiates most of its energy in the middle of the visible spectrum, in the orange and yellow, with less at either end, in the red and violet. Our eyes have evolved to make good use of the light that is available, which is why it is just this range of electromagnetic radiation that is visible to us. So there is less violet light available to be scattered than there is blue light. But the way our eyes have evolved affects the way we perceive the scattered light.

There are only three kinds of receptors, also known as cones, in our eyes, which respond most strongly to either red, green or blue wavelengths, sending signals to our brains that are interpreted as a variety of colours depending on the proportion of each of these three basic tints. But each of these receptors actually responds to a range of wavelengths, with peaks close to 564 nm (red), 534 nm (green) and 420 nm (blue). The blue cones are stimulated most strongly by blue light, but also, to a lesser extent, by other colours. Similarly, the other cones are stimulated by a range of wavelengths. The green cones are stimulated a little bit by the blue light, and if it were simply the case that blue light is scattered the most, then the sky would look greenish-blue to our eyes. But the violet light is also being scattered, and through a quirk of biochemistry, the red cones are a bit more sensitive to violet light than the green cones are. Overall, the red and green cones are roughly equally stimulated by the light from the sky. The result is that the contribution of 'green' stimulated by blue light and the contribution of 'red' stimulated by violet light cancel each other out, and our brains simply perceive blue. Which is just about the end of the story of why our sky is blue, but not quite the end of the story of blue skies in the Solar System.

When astronomers first received colour images from the surface of Mars, returned by the first Viking Lander mission at the end of February 1997, they were surprised to find that the sky looked red. They soon realised that this was because the images were obtained in the aftermath of a storm that had thrown large quantities of red dust up into the atmosphere. But even when the dust from the storm cleared, they found that the sky on Mars looks very different from the sky on Earth, and this can also be explained in terms of Rayleigh scattering.

The air on Mars is very thin – less than 1 per cent as dense at the surface as the atmosphere of the Earth – and this means that there are very few molecules around to do the scattering. Other things being equal, the sky in daytime on Mars would be a very pale blue. But other things are not equal. Mars is so dry and dusty that there is always a haze of dust suspended in the air, and these dust particles (very fine, but much larger than molecules) bounce enough sunlight around from dust grain to dust grain, like balls bouncing around in a pinball machine, to give what some people describe as a 'butterscotch' tint – actually yellow – to the Martian sky. But sunsets (and sunrises) are different. When the Sun is low on the Martian horizon, the light has further to travel through the thin atmosphere, and it encounters enough molecules for Rayleigh scattering to begin to be effective. So sunsets on Mars are blue!

If you want to see a spectacularly blue sky, however, the best place to be is suspended from is a balloon floating above the clouds of the planet Jupiter. NASA's Galileo spacecraft was launched from the space shuttle Atlantis in October 1989, and arrived at Jupiter in December 1995. It carried a probe to investigate the atmosphere of Jupiter, which was released from the main spacecraft on 13 July 1995, when it was still about 80 million kilometres from the giant planet, and put on a trajectory calculated in accordance with Newton's laws of motion. The probe hit the atmosphere of Jupiter on 7 December 1995, and was slowed by a 2.5-meter-diameter parachute, enabling it to send back data for 58 minutes, measuring pressures 230 times greater than those at sea level on Earth, before it was crushed. At such high pressures, which correspond to high density, Rayleigh scattering is very effective, with the result that the sky is a brilliant bright blue. Newton, Tyndall, Rayleigh and Einstein would surely have been delighted by the discovery.

FURTHER READING

Easy stuff

George Gamow, *A Star Called the Sun*, Viking, New York, 1964

John Gribbin and Mary Gribbin, *How Far Is Up?: The Men Who Measured the Universe*, Icon, London, 2003

Iain Stewart and John Lynch, *Earth: The Power of the Planet*, BBC, London, 2007

Rachel Carson, *The Sea Around Us*, Oxford University Press, Oxford, 1951

Not-so-easy stuff

Edward Harrison, *Cosmology: The Science of the Universe*, Cambridge University Press, Cambridge, 1981

Roland Jackson, *The Ascent of John Tyndall: Victorian Scientist, Mountaineer, and Public Intellectual*, Oxford University Press, Oxford, 2018

Rudolf Kippenhahn, *100 Billion Suns: The Birth, Life and Death of the Stars*, Weidenfeld & Nicolson, London, 1983

Stephen Mason, *Chemical Evolution: Origins of the Elements, Molecules and Living Systems*, Clarendon Press, Oxford, 1991

Hard stuff

Ken Croswell, *The Alchemy of the Heavens: Searching for Meaning in the Milky Way*, Anchor, New York, 1995

Ian Morison, *Introduction to Astronomy and Cosmology*, Wiley, New York, 2008

Fun stuff

George Gamow, *Mr Tompkins in Paperback*, Cambridge University Press, Cambridge reprint edition, 2012

John Gribbin and Mary Gribbin, *On the Origin of Evolution: Tracing 'Darwin's Dangerous Idea' from Aristotle to DNA*, Collins, London, 2020

SEVEN PILLARS OF SCIENCE

The Incredible Lightness of Ice,
and Other Scientific Surprises

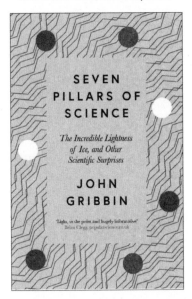

John Gribbin presents a tour of seven fundamental scientific truths that underpin our very existence.

These 'pillars of science' also defy common sense. For example, solid things are mostly empty space, so how do they hold together? There appears to be no special 'life force', so how do we distinguish living things from inanimate objects? And why does ice float on water, when most solids don't? You might think that question hardly needs asking, and yet if ice didn't float, life on Earth would never have happened.

The answers to all of these questions were sensational in their day, and some still are. Throughout history, science has been able to think the unthinkable – and Gribbin brilliantly shows the surprising secrets on which our understanding of life is based.

ISBN 978-178578-858-1

£9.99

EIGHT IMPROBABLE POSSIBILITIES

*The Mystery of the Moon, and Other
Implausible Scientific Truths*

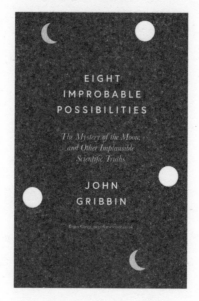

John Gribbin turns his attention to
some of the mind-bendingly improbable
truths of science, such as:

The Moon and Sun look the same size on the
sky – but only at the moment of geological time
that we are here to notice it; water swirling in a
bucket knows how all the matter in the distant
galaxies of the Universe is distributed; and
without the stabilising influence of the Moon,
life forms like us could never have evolved.

As Gribbin concludes: 'Once you have eliminated the
impossible, whatever is left, however improbable, is
certainly *possible*, in the light of present knowledge.'

ISBN 978-178578-979-3

£9.99